Word Problems with Fractions

Paul R. Robbins and Sharon K. Hauge

illustrated by
Mike Kupperman and Lois Leonard Stock

J. WESTON
WALCH
PUBLISHER
Portland, Maine

User's Guide
to
Walch Reproducible Books

As part of our general effort to provide educational materials which are as practical and economical as possible, we have designated this publication a "reproducible book." The designation means that purchase of the book includes purchase of the right to limited reproduction of all pages on which this symbol appears:

Here is the basic Walch policy: We grant to individual purchasers of this book the right to make sufficient copies of reproducible pages for use by all students of a single teacher. This permission is limited to a single teacher, and does not apply to entire schools or school systems, so institutions purchasing the book should pass the permission on to a single teacher. Copying of the book or its parts for resale is prohibited.

Any questions regarding this policy or requests to purchase further reproduction rights should be addressed to:

Permissions Editor
J. Weston Walch, Publisher
321 Valley Street • P. O. Box 658
Portland, Maine 04104-0658

1 2 3 4 5 6 7 8 9 10

ISBN 0-8251-3750-0

Printed in the United States of America

Contents

Chapter 2. Adding and Subtracting Fractions

Chapter 3. Addition and Subtraction of Fractions That Have Unlike Denominators

Chapter 6. Dividing with Fractions

Chapter 7. Advanced Problems That Require Two or More Different Operations

To the Teacher

Here's a book designed to build student skills in two areas of concern for most teachers: working with fractions and applying arithmetic skills through word problems.

Word Problems with Fractions parallels two other books by Paul R. Robbins and Sharon K. Hauge, *Word Problems with Whole Numbers* and *Word Problems with Decimals, Proportions and Percents*. The books are not dependent on one another, but they can be used together very well.

This series of books came into existence at the urging of J. Weston Walch, the founder of J. Weston Walch, Publisher. Mr. Walch recognized the need to provide materials for students that would not only teach the fundamentals of arithmetic but would also show the students how to use these skills to solve word problems. He wanted texts that would help students learn these skills while keeping the students engaged and interested in learning.

The three books for solving word problems emerged as a way of meeting this challenging task. We were very pleased that the approach we used won acceptance by many classroom teachers as a tool for teaching problem-solving skills to their students. The books have remained staples in the Walch catalog since their publication. Their reproducible format has kept them perenniel favorites among veteran teachers and those new to the field.

It is now time for a new edition of these texts. There are a number of reasons for this decision. One reason has to do with the prices mentioned in many of the word problems in the texts. To keep the word problems credible to the students, we had to use new, realistic prices. A second reason for the new edition is the explosion of new technologies that entered the lives of young people. We wanted to include word problems that used these technologies as well as new information and ideas that have come from science. Third, many students are now using hand-held calculators. We believe it is important to show students how to use calculators as tools for solving word problems.

With these needs in mind, we offer the second edition of *Word Problems with Fractions*.

Word Problems with Fractions is written at a level which almost all middle school students will handle comfortably. It presents a series of problems that young people will find not only interesting but worth trying to solve. And it presents the subject of fractions with rare lucidity and conciseness.

We hope that you will continue to find *Word Problems with Fractions* useful in your classroom teaching. We welcome your comments.

To the Student

Word Problems with Fractions is the second volume in our series of books that explain how to solve word problems in basic mathematics. In the other books, we cover word problems that use whole numbers and decimals, proportions, and percents. In this text, we shall show you how to solve problems that use fractions.

In the earlier book, *Word Problems with Whole Numbers*, we explained in detail how to recognize which operations of arithmetic are needed to solve a particular problem; that is, whether you need to add, subtract, multiply or divide to find the correct answer. We did this by pointing out certain key words, phrases or ideas that are presented in the problem that act as signals or guides to help you decide what to do. In this text, we shall continue in this manner. However, we shall be briefer, since we have discussed some of these ideas before.

Introduction to Fractions

Teacher Notes

This chapter introduces students to the basics of fractions in a thorough, step-by-step manner. It assumes no prior knowledge, and while speaking to students at their own level, it does not oversimplify. Each term is defined, each concept is carefully explained, and each step in a procedure clearly proceeds from the previous step and leads to the next. The many illustrations clarify the concepts under discussion. Even students who have had no exposure whatever to fractions should be comfortable with this approach.

Chapter 1 covers terms and definitions, fraction reading, ways to represent fractions including circle graphs, names of units of measurement, including metric (so that students learn to give word problem answers in the correct units), ratios, proper vs. improper fractions, and reducing to lowest terms. After each section of instructional material, Word Problems for Practice give students the chance to apply the material to basic problem solving. (The answers, by section, appear below.) In addition, Handy Rules are introduced periodically in order to provide students with reference points and reminders. These lessons cover a lot of ground, and the Handy Rules digest the concepts so that students won't feel overwhelmed. (A complete reproducible list of the rules appears at the end of this teacher material.) Drills for Skill help students gain speed and proficiency in working with fractions. (All of these features appear in every chapter.) Organizing drillwork into a competition can make it more interesting for students. Finally, extra enrichment is provided by sections such as Some Fascinating Ratios, Further Explorations, and Some History About Fractions.

Answers

Word Problems for Practice I

1. $\frac{1}{7}$, **2.** $\frac{5}{8}$, **3.** $\frac{1}{3}$, **4.** $\frac{1}{4}$, **5.** $\frac{4}{8}$, **6.** $\frac{1}{3}$, **7.** $\frac{2}{3}$, **8.** $\frac{1}{13}$. **A Fish Story:** $\frac{1}{2}$

Word Problems for Practice II

1. $\frac{10}{75}$, **2.** $\frac{1}{26}$, **3.** $\frac{7}{60}$, **4.** $\frac{4}{20}$, **5.** $\frac{18}{28}$, **6.** $\frac{19}{32}$, **7.** $\frac{7}{24}$, **8.** $\frac{5}{50}$, **9.** $\frac{40}{100}$.

Showing Fractional Parts with a Circle Graph: 1. $\frac{2}{8}$ **2.** $\frac{1}{8}$ **3.** $\frac{2}{8}$

Word Problems for Practice III

1. $\frac{9}{16}$, **2.** students $\frac{900}{960}$, teachers $\frac{45}{960}$, other fields $\frac{15}{960}$, not students $\frac{60}{960}$, **3.** infielders $\frac{5}{11}$, outfielders $\frac{4}{11}$, pitcher $\frac{1}{11}$, catcher $\frac{1}{11}$, **4.** classical $\frac{4}{19}$, rock $\frac{5}{19}$, country $\frac{3}{19}$, jazz $\frac{2}{19}$, **5.** $\frac{1}{12}$, **6.** $\frac{11}{20}$

Word Problems for Practice IV-A

1. $\frac{12{,}000}{16{,}000}$, **2.** $\frac{2}{12}$, **3.** $\frac{150}{300}$, **4.** $\frac{365}{687}$, **5.** $\frac{1}{3}$, **6.** $\frac{4}{206}$, **7.** $\frac{20}{80}$

Word Problems for Practice IV-B

1. $\frac{11}{36}$, **2.** $\frac{50}{100}$, **3.** $\frac{60}{1{,}000}$, **4.** $\frac{700}{2{,}000}$, **5.** $\frac{5{,}000}{50}$, **6.** $\frac{1}{8}$

Word Problems for Practice V

1. $\frac{19}{5}$, **2.** $21\frac{7}{8}$ lbs., **3.** $\frac{19}{4}$, $4\frac{3}{4}$, **4.** $\frac{55}{45}$, $1\frac{10}{45}$, **5.** $\frac{4}{3}$, $1\frac{1}{3}$, **6.** George $\frac{17}{5}$, Joe $\frac{6}{10}$, Sally $\frac{23}{2}$, Mitzi $\frac{1}{23}$, improper fractions: George, Sally, mixed numbers $3\frac{2}{5}$, $11\frac{1}{2}$.

Drill for Skill I

1. a. 4, **b.** 2, **c.** 2, **d.** 25, **2. a.** $2\frac{2}{3}$, **b.** $1\frac{1}{5}$, **c.** $2\frac{1}{25}$, **d.** $24\frac{1}{3}$, **3. a.** $\frac{9}{5}$, **b.** $\frac{29}{10}$, **c.** $\frac{23}{6}$, **d.** $\frac{204}{7}$

Drill for Skill II

1. a. $\frac{2}{10}$, **b.** $\frac{4}{10}$, **c.** $\frac{6}{20}$, **d.** $\frac{8}{6}$, **e.** $\frac{10}{12}$, **f.** $\frac{14}{16}$, **2. a.** $\frac{3}{4}$, **b.** $\frac{2}{3}$, **c.** $\frac{3}{4}$, **d.** $\frac{1}{2}$, **e.** $\frac{3}{4}$, **f.** $\frac{3}{25}$, **3.** $\frac{200}{10{,}000}$, $\frac{1}{50}$, **4.** $\frac{1{,}340}{5{,}280}$, $\frac{67}{264}$

Name ______________________________

Date ______________________________

Reproducible

Introduction to Fractions

This material is all about fractions. We will explain how to add, subtract, multiply, and divide fractions and how to use these techniques to solve word problems. We will also talk about reducing fractions and working with mixed numbers. Because many people have trouble with fractions, we will start off very carefully and try to present a clear idea of just what fractions are and what they mean. To do this, we will begin with some things we all know about from everyday experience. For example, let's start with the idea of one half ($\frac{1}{2}$). What does $\frac{1}{2}$ mean?

There are a lot of ways we use one half. One meaning is "halfway." If you were driving from Washington, D.C. to California, you would be **halfway there** when you reached Kansas.

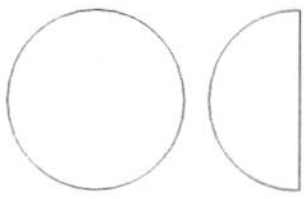

Think of a full moon—nice, round, and yellow.

Now think of half a moon.

Think of a bottle of cola. Drink half of it. What's left? 

Or look at the people in this picture. One-half are males and one-half are females.

Now let's talk about one quarter ($\frac{1}{4}$). Instead of a half ($\frac{1}{2}$) dollar, we have: 

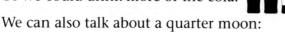

Or we could drink more of the cola: 

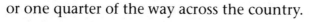

We can also talk about a quarter moon:

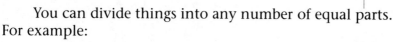

or one quarter of the way across the country.

You can divide things into any number of equal parts. For example:

This young man has climbed about two thirds ($\frac{2}{3}$) of the way up to the top of the hill.

A dime is one tenth ($\frac{1}{10}$) of a dollar.

My gasoline tank is three quarters ($\frac{3}{4}$) full. My stock was down seven eights ($\frac{7}{8}$) of a point.

If you live in the United States, you are one two-hundred-sixty-five-millionth ($\frac{1}{265,000,000}$) of the population of the United States.

The Numerator and the Denominator

By now, you have undoubtedly discovered that a fraction has two parts. ($^{1}/_{2}$, $^{1}/_{4}$, $^{2}/_{3}$, $^{1}/_{10}$, $^{1}/_{100}$, $^{1}/_{265,000,000}$)

You write a fraction by putting one number above the line and one number below the line. The number above the line is called the **numerator**. The number below the line is called the **denominator**.

$^{2}/_{3}$ $\qquad$ $^{\text{Numerator}}/_{\text{Denominator}}$

The numerator can be any whole number and the denominator can be any whole number, except zero.

Sometimes the numerator and the denominator are called the **terms of the fraction**.

A Guide to Reading Fractions

1. First, read the whole number in the numerator.

Then, read the whole number in the denominator,

(a) adding "-th" if the numerator equals 1

(b) or adding "-ths" if the numerator is greater than 1.

Examples: $^{1}/_{6}$ one six**th**; $^{5}/_{6}$ five six**ths**

While the above rule is helpful, there are a number of exceptions to it. Here are five common exceptions.

(a) half: $^{1}/_{2}$ one half
halves: $^{3}/_{2}$ three halves

(b) third: $^{1}/_{3}$ one third
thirds: $^{2}/_{3}$ two thirds

(c) fifth: $^{1}/_{5}$ one fifth
fifths: $^{2}/_{5}$ two fifths

(d) first: $^{1}/_{21}$ one twenty-first
firsts: $^{3}/_{21}$ three twenty-firsts

(e) secondth: $^{1}/_{32}$ one thirty-secondth
secondths: $^{3}/_{32}$ three thirty-secondths

2. If the number in the denominator ends in "y", change "y" to "ie" before adding **th** or **ths**.

Example: $^{1}/_{40}$ one fortieth

Name ______________________________

Date ______________________________

Reproducible

Introduction to Fractions

Uses of Fractions

While a common fraction has only one mathematical definition, one can look at the ways fractions are used in problems from somewhat different viewpoints. Here are three of the ways fractions are used.

A. Fractions can be used to show that a whole thing or unit has been broken up into a certain number of equal parts and that we have a special interest in some of these parts.

B. Fractions can be used to represent one or more equal parts of a total collection of units.

C. Fractions can be used to compare two quantities.

Let's try to make these ideas clearer. Let's begin with the first one. We will look at the others in later lessons.

You can break up almost anything into equal parts. Take a football field. It is divided into one hundred equal yards. Let's suppose your team is on your opponent's one-yard line. You have only one more yard to go and you score. What part is that one yard of the football field? If you said $^1/_{100}$ you are right.

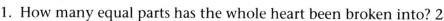

A Handy Rule for Writing Fractions (A)

To write a fraction which shows that one whole thing has been broken into a certain number of equal parts, and that we have a special interest in some of these parts:

1. First, **ASK** how many equal parts the whole thing has been broken into.
2. **WRITE** this number and **DRAW** a line above it.
3. Next, **ASK** in how many of these parts do we have a special interest?
4. **WRITE** this number above the fraction line.

The following examples illustrate this idea.

Something has been broken into 2 equal parts.

I have one of these parts.

One Half

$^1/_2$

1. How many equal parts has the whole heart been broken into? 2
2. $/_2$
3. How many of these parts do we have special interest in? 1
4. $^1/_2$

Something has been broken into 3 equal parts.
I have two of these parts.
Something has been broken into 6 equal parts.
I have five of these parts.

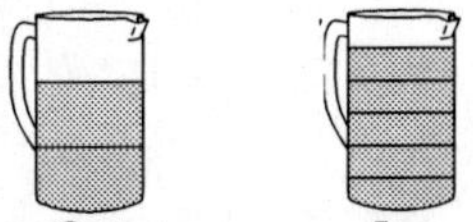

$2/3$ $5/6$

Two Thirds Five Sixths

Example:	A house has been divided into 4 equal rooms. What fraction of the house is one room?
Solution:	The whole thing is the house. It has been divided into 4 equal rooms. Hence, 4 should be written below the line or in the denominator. You are particularly concerned with 1 of these rooms, or **one** of the equal parts. Therefore 1 should be written above the line or in the numerator. The answer is $1/4$.

Is this idea clear? Try these exercises and see.

Word Problems for Practice (I)

1. A week is divided into 7 days. What fraction of a week is 1 day?
2. A chocolate bar was divided into 8 equal parts. What fraction of the bar are 5 of these parts?
3. The design of a space shuttle for a future space exploration called for the shuttle to be divided into 3 equal sections. The first section would be the living quarters for the men and women who would navigate the shuttle. The second section was to be used for scientific studies. The third section would be storage room for supplies. What fraction of the space shuttle would be used for living quarters?
4. A football game was divided into 4 periods of equal length. After the first period of the game was over, what fraction of the game had been completed?
5. Beth and Keisha invited their boyfriends out for a pizza. The pizza was divided into 8 equal pieces. After the 4 friends had each eaten 1 piece, what fraction of the pizza had been eaten?
6. A student had a part-time job. He received a take-home pay check of $120 each month. He split the money up equally into 3 parts, using the money to pay for snacks, compact discs, and to take out his girlfriend. What fraction of his pay check did he use for snacks?

7. Dr. Bauer bought a battery for his car. The battery was supposed to last for 3 years. The battery died after 2 years. For what part of its expected life did the battery work?

8. For most children, the school experience is 13 years long, kindergarten through Grade 12 (the senior year of high school). Kevin has just completed kindergarten. What part of his school experience has he completed?

A Fish Story

Janet received an aquarium for her birthday. She bought two types of fish to put into the aquarium, mollies and guppies. Just before she put the fish into the water, she was told by a friend that it wasn't a good idea because the mollies would eat the guppies for breakfast. She decided to put a partition in the aquarium dividing the aquarium into 2 equal parts, one part for the mollies and one part for the guppies. What fraction of the aquarium was to be a home for the guppies?

Using Fractions to Represent One or More Equal Parts of a Total Collection of Units

In the last lesson, we began with a single thing or unit which was divided into a number of equal parts. We wrote fractions to show how one or more of these equal parts was related to the whole thing.

Now we will shift our view of fractions. Instead of looking at a single unit, we will look at a collection of several units. We will use fractions to represent one or more equal parts of the total collection. We will show you how to do this.

Imagine that you have a collection of objects in front of you. Let's say that it is a group of oranges. You count the oranges and you find there is a total of 12 oranges.

Now if you put your hand on 2 of the oranges, you could ask, what part of the total (12 oranges) are the 2 oranges you are touching? You can give this answer as a fraction. **A fraction, then, can be used to show the relationship of one or more equal parts of a collection to the total collection.**

A Handy Rule for Writing Fractions (B)

To show the relationship of one or more equal parts of a collection to the total collection:

1. First, find out how many things there are in the **total** collection. In the illustration on page 6 you can do this by simply counting the oranges, reaching a total of 12.
2. Write this total in the denominator $/_{12}$.
3. Then ask, "In how many parts of the total collection am I particularly interested?" (That would be the 2 oranges you are touching.)
4. Write the number in the numerator. Your answer is $^{2}/_{12}$.

Let's try another example.

Example:	A jigsaw puzzle was composed of 500 separate pieces. If you had put 35 pieces together, what part of the total number of pieces would you have completed?
Solution:	(1) There are 500 pieces in the total puzzle. (2) 500 should be written in the denominator: $/_{500}$. (3) We are concerned with 35 of these pieces. (4) Write 35 in the numerator. Answer: $^{35}/_{500}$

Word Problems for Practice (II)

1. A boy had been saving coins. He spread the coins in front of him and counted 75 different coins. Ten of the coins were dimes. What fraction of the total collection were dimes? ___________
2. The letter "A" is what part of the total number of letters that make up the English alphabet? ___________
3. Mary Ann looked through an old chest in her father's attic and found a bunch of old comic books dating back to the 1930's and 1940's. There were 60 comic books in all. Seven of the comic books turned out to be rare and were worth over $100 each. What fraction of the collection of comic books were rare? ___________

4. A teacher was making up a science test. She made up 20 questions, then threw away 4 because they were too hard. What part of the original test items did she throw away? __________

5. Imagine you are playing Monopoly™ with a friend. There are 28 pieces of property around the board. (You know them—Boardwalk, Park Place, the Electric Company). You are way ahead in the game. You own 18 of the pieces, while your friend has 10. What fraction of the total number of pieces do you own? __________

6. On the first day of school, a history teacher looked over his class roll. He counted 32 students. However, only 19 students actually showed up for class. What fraction of his total class enrollment was present? __________

7. Ruth became interested in learning about the stars and planets. She went to the library and found they had been collecting the monthly magazine *Sky and Telescope* for a period of 24 months. She started at the beginning and read the first 7 issues. What part of the collection had she read?

   ____

8. John had learned that the nature of many jobs has changed, and that new technical skills were needed to get a good job. He sent out questionnaires to the top 50 companies in his community to ask about the training and skills the company required of its employees. Sadly, only 5 companies responded. What fraction of the companies responded? __________

9. Scientists working in Africa have discovered stone tools made by people many thousands of years ago. Some of the stone tools were used for breaking objects and others for scraping things. If in a sample of 100 stone tools, 40 were identified as scrapers, what fraction of the total number of stone tools was scrapers? __________

Showing Fractional Parts with a Circle Graph

The circle graph, sometimes called a "pie chart" or "pie graph," represents the portion of Bill's day between the time he comes home from school and the time he goes to bed. The circle is divided into equal parts. Each of these equal parts represents one hour of time. If you count these parts, you will see there are 8 of them. Hence, the total amount of time represented by the circle graph is 8 hours.

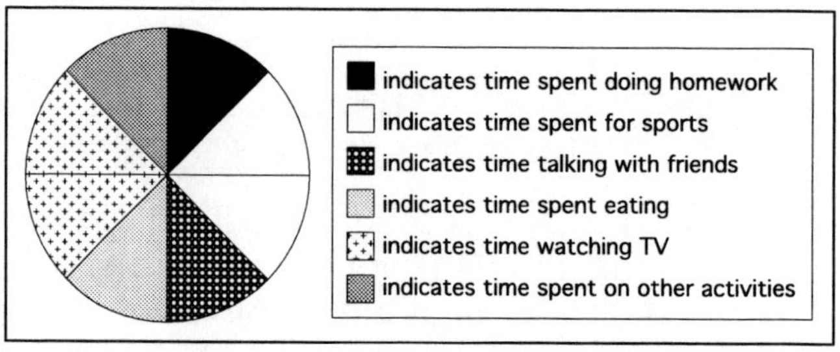

SOME QUESTIONS

1. What fraction of the 8 hours did Bill spend for sports? __________
2. What fraction of the time did Bill spend talking with his friends? ________
3. What fraction of the time did Bill spend watching television? __________

In the space below, try to make a pie graph that shows your own after-school activities.

Another Handy Rule (B-1)

When a fraction is used to show a part of the total, there are times that we must **add** in order to find out how many there are in the total. Here is such an example.

Example:	Gasohol is a fuel for cars that is made by mixing a small amount of alcohol with a large amount of gasoline. The exact mixture is 1 gallon of alcohol and 9 gallons of gasoline. What part of the total mixture is alcohol? Write this as a fraction.
Solution:	(1) In this problem the total is 9 gallons of gasoline + 1 gallon of alcohol = 10 gallons. (2) So we write 10 in the denominator: $\frac{\ }{10}$. (3) In reading the question, you can see that you are concerned with the number of gallons of alcohol. There is 1 gallon of alcohol. (4) So we write 1 in the numerator: $\frac{1}{10}$. The answer is $\frac{1}{10}$.

Word Problems for Practice (III)

1. A professional football team won 9 games and lost 7 games during the entire season. Write a fraction that shows what part the number of games won was of the total number of games played? __________

2. In Jefferson High School, there were 900 students, 45 teachers, and 15 other people such as secretaries and janitors. What fraction of the persons in the school were students? __________ teachers? __________ worked in other jobs? __________ What fraction of the total were not students? __________

3. There are nine players on a baseball team: 4 infielders, 3 outfielders, a pitcher and a catcher. During a game, the infielders made 5 hits, the outfielders 4 hits, and the pitcher and catcher each had 1 hit. Write a fraction that would show what part of the total hits were made by the infielders. Now do this for the outfielders; the pitcher; and the catcher. __________ __________ __________

4. During the first hour of business, the Harmony Compact Disc shop sold the following number of compact discs: 4 playing classical music; 5 playing rock music; 3 playing country music; 2 playing jazz; 5 playing other kinds of music. Write a fraction showing what part of the total number of compact discs were classical music; rock music; country music; jazz. __________ __________ __________ __________

5. At a neighborhood dog show, the following dogs were entered: 3 poodles; 1 cocker spaniel; 2 dachshunds; 1 very large, tough-looking Great Dane with sharp teeth; 5 mongrels. If each dog had the same chance of winning, what fraction represents the chance that each dog had of winning (think "1 out of what?"). (Your answer is called the **probability** that a particular dog will win.) __________ (By the way, the dog that won all the votes was the Great Dane. Nobody wanted to get on the wrong side of his owner.)

6. Mr. Hernandez decided to get internet service for his computer. During his first month of internet access, his son Migel used the internet for 5 hours, and his daughter Trina used the internet for 6 hours. Mr. Hernandez used it for 9 hours. What fraction of the total internet time used was used by his two children? __________

Let's Stop To Think About Measures

In some of the problems we have worked, we have used units of measure like **yards** (in measuring the length of a football field) and **gallons** (in our problem about gasohol). Yards and gallons—as well as **inches, feet, miles,** and **pounds**—are units of measure commonly used in the United States.

In many of our problems, we will also be using measures from the **metric system**, such as meters and liters. The metric system is widely used throughout the world and is very important in science. Because many of our readers may have grown up using only one of these systems of measurement, the other system may seem strange. So we've included a handy guide to help you understand the units we'll be using from both systems of measurement. Study the guide before you go on to the next section on ratio.

A Guide to Units of Measurement

For those readers who have grown up with units like **inches, pounds,** and **gallons**, here are some easy ways to understand the metric terms we will use.

1. **Liter.** The problem may say, "She poured out half of a liter bottle of cola." What is a liter? A liter is just about the same size as a quart. When you see the word liter, think of a quart of milk.
2. **Meter.** The problem may say, "The board is two meters long." How long is a meter? Think of an overgrown yardstick. Imagine a yardstick about 39 inches long instead of 36 inches.
3. **Kilometer.** The problem may say, "The highway is 15 kilometers in length." The kilometer is a measure for longer distances. Picture in your mind riding in a car for half a mile. A kilometer is just a little more than that.
4. **Gram.** The problem may say, "She poured 5 grams of sulphur into a test tube." A gram is a measure of weight. How heavy is a gram? Not heavy at all. Think of something very light. Put a paper clip in your hand. A paper clip weighs about a gram.

For those readers who have grown up with the metric system, here are some ways to understand other units of measurements.

5. **Inch.** Roughly the distance across your eye.
6. **Foot.** About the length of a large man's shoe.
7. **Yard.** A slightly shortened meter.
8. **Mile.** A little less than two kilometers.
9. **Quart.** Just a little less than a liter.
10. **Gallon.** Slightly less than four liters.
11. **Pound.** Just a bit lighter than $\frac{1}{2}$ kilogram.

Name ______________________________

Date ______________________________

Reproducible

Introduction to Fractions

Using a Fraction to Compare Quantities: Ratios

Often it is necessary to compare two quantities. These quantities could be the heights of two buildings, the sizes of two salaries, the speeds with which two rockets hurtle through space, or just about anything you can think of that uses numbers.

When two quantities are compared by writing the measure of one quantity over the measure of the other quantity, we have a fraction; and the fraction is called a **ratio**.

Sometimes the things we are comparing are measured in the same unit, such as:

two buildings measured in **meters**
two salaries measured in **dollars**
two elephants measured in **tons**.

Sometimes, however, the things you are comparing are measured in different units, such as: a **quart** of **ice cream** and a **gallon** of **ice cream**; **time** in **seconds** and **time** in **minutes**.

Two Handy Rules for Writing Ratios (C)

Here is how to write a ratio:

I. If the things you are comparing are expressed in the *same* unit of measure,

1. write the quantity which follows that word **to** in the denominator.
2. write the other quantity in the numerator.

Example:	During the 1930's a postage stamp for first class mail cost 3 cents. In 1999 a postage stamp for first class mail cost 33 cents. What is the ratio of the old price to the new price?
Solution:	We are comparing cents with cents.

1. We want the ratio of 3 cents to 33 cents. "Thirty-three" is after the word "to." So 33 is written in the denominator: $/_{33}$.
2. The other number is 3, so 3 is written in the numerator: $^{3}/_{33}$.
   The answer is $^{3}/_{33}$. This answer means that the old price is three thirty-thirds as large as the new price.

Now let's suppose, instead of a 3-cent stamp and a 33-cent stamp, you have a 75-cent stamp and a $1.25 stamp. Now you have **cents** and **dollars** which are **different** units. What do you do now?

II. If the measurements of the things you are comparing are given in different units of measure, such as in cents and dollars, first change the measurements of the things you are comparing into the smaller unit of measure. Then write the ratio.

Suppose, for example, that you want to write the ratio of 75 cents to $1.25.

1. You have cents and dollars. A cent is a smaller unit of measure than a dollar. First you need to express both quantities: 75 cents and $1.25 in cents. Seventy-five cents is already expressed in cents. To change $1.25 into cents, think: "One dollar and twenty-five cents is 100 cents + 25 cents or 125 cents." So, you need to write the ratio 75 cents to 125 cents.
2. Write the quality that comes after the word "to" in the denominator: $/_{125}$.
3. Write the other quantity in the numerator: $^{75}/_{125}$.

Word Problems for Practice (IV-A)

Try these problems. You will see that the things which are compared are measured in the same unit.

1. Car A sold for $16,000. Car B sold for $12,000. What is the ratio of the selling price of Car B to Car A? __________
2. The neighborhood kids use a long, steep hill for sledding in winter. It takes 2 minutes to go down the snow-covered hill on a sled and 12 minutes to walk back up the hill. What is the ratio of the time going down the hill to the time going up the hill? __________
3. Jerry launched his 4-foot glider into the air with a strong tail wind blowing behind it. It soared 300 meters. Then, he launched the glider a second time without the tail wind and it soared only 150 meters. What is the ratio of the distance the glider traveled without the tail wind to the distance the glider traveled with the tail wind? __________
4. The planet Earth orbits the sun in 365 days. The planet Mars orbits the sun in 687 days. What is the ratio of the time it takes Earth to orbit the sun to the time it takes Mars to orbit the sun? __________

5. Have you ever used frozen orange concentrate to make orange juice? The instructions on many cans ask you to use one can of orange concentrate and 3 cans of water. What is the ratio of orange concentrate to water?

    ____

6. There are 206 bones in the human body. Four of these bones are in the ear. What is the ratio of the number of bones in the ear to the number of bones in the human body? __________

7. The county recreation department sponsored a bicycle ride through the most scenic areas of the county. For those riders who wanted a long trip, the route was 80 kilometers. For the people who wanted to ride a shorter distance, the department laid out a 20-kilometer route. What is the ratio of the shorter route to the longer route? __________

Word Problems for Practice (IV-B)

Now try these problems. Here the things for which you are to write ratios are measured in different units.

1. Denise bought 2 tote bags at the beach. The first was huge, 3 feet tall, and you could stuff beach towels and almost anything else into it. The second bag was smaller, measuring only 11 inches tall. What was the ratio of the shorter bag to the taller bag? (Hint: 1 foot equals 12 inches.) __________
2. What is the ratio of 50 years to a century? __________
3. What is the ratio of 60 meters to 1 kilometer? (Hint: 1 kilometer equals 1000 meters.) __________
4. The length of the first nature trail is 700 meters. The length of the second nature trail is 2 kilometers. What is the ratio of the length of the first trail to the length of the second trail? __________
5. What is the ratio of 50 dollars to 50 cents? __________
6. What is the ratio of one quart to 2 gallons? (Hint: 1 gallon equals 4 quarts.)

    ____

Some Fascinating Ratios

Look at the numbers in the line below

1, 1, 2, 3, 5, 8, 13, 21, 34, 55, . . .

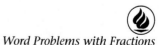

Do you see a pattern in this row of numbers? If you can figure out the pattern, you can guess what the next number in the row will be. What is your guess? If you guessed 89, you are correct.

Still can't see it? Well, if not, we'll help you.

Add the first two numbers in the row, 1 + 1. The sum 2 is the same as the third number in the row.

Now, add the second and third numbers in the row, 1 + 2. The sum 3 is the same as the fourth number in the row.

Do you see that from now on, the next number in the row can always be found by adding together the two numbers which appear just before it?

2 + 3 = 5, 3 + 5 = 8, . . . Continue, and you will see that 34 + 55 = 89.

The numbers which appear in the pattern

1, 1, 2, 3, 5, 8, 13, 21, 34, 55, 89, . . . can be found in many places. The number of petals of most flowers is a number in this pattern. Here are some examples. Impatiens have 5 petals. Many delphiniums have 8; marigolds, 13; asters, 21. Usually daisies have 34, 55, or 89 petals. Most clovers have 3 leaves—another number in our curious pattern. (Maybe, that's why you're considered lucky if you happen to find a 4-leaf clover!)

Ratios of pairs of numbers in the pattern

1, 1, 2, 3, 5, 8, 13, 21, 34, 55, 89, . . . appear in visual art, architecture, painting, sculpture, music, and nature.

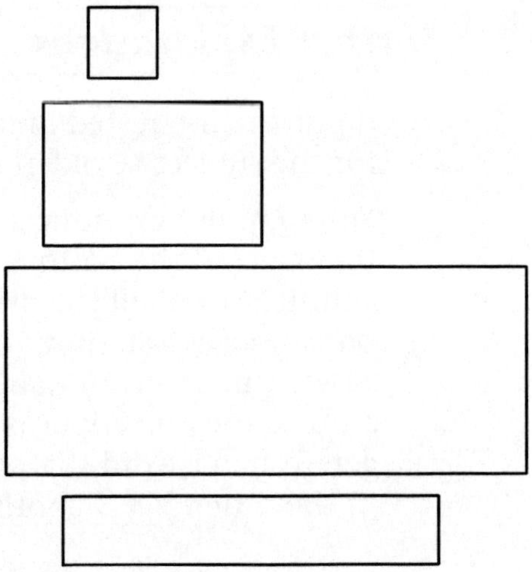

Let's consider some familiar objects that are shaped like rectangles. In a 3 by 5 note card, the ratio of the width to the length is $^3/_5$. In a 5 by 8 note card, the ratio of the width to the length is $^5/_8$. What is the ratio of the width to the length of an American flag? Look at the fronts of cereal boxes. What is the ratio of their width to their length? Did you find any ratios that were ratios of numbers in our curious pattern?

Now look at the pictures to the right.

Which rectangle looks best to you? Psychologists have asked people which of these rectangles they found most pleasing. Most of the people the psychologists questioned found the second rectangle, the one whose dimensions form a $^5/_8$ ratio, to be the most pleasing. The ratio $^5/_8$ appears many times in architecture, painting, sculpture, and music. The front of the beautiful Greek temple, which is called the Parthenon, can almost be framed by a rectangle whose width to length ratio is $^5/_8$. The figure of St. Jerome (minus his arm) in Leonardo da Vinci's painting can almost be framed by a rectangle whose width to height ratio is $^5/_8$. Some figures are sculpted so that the ratio of the distance from the figure's waist to its feet, to the total height of the figure is in the ratio of $^5/_8$. For those of you who are interested in music, the ratio of the number of vibrations per second of the note C to the number of vibrations per second of the note E is $^5/_8$.

Ratios of the numbers in our curious pattern 1, 1, 2, 3, 5, 8, 13, 21, 34, 55, . . . also appear in nature. The picture at the right shows what we saw when we looked at the top of a cactus plant and counted the spirals going around the cactus plant in one direction. We got 13 spirals. When we counted the spirals going around the cactus in the other direction, we got 21. The ratio of our smaller count to our larger count is $^{13}/_{21}$, which is the ratio of a pair of numbers in our curious pattern.

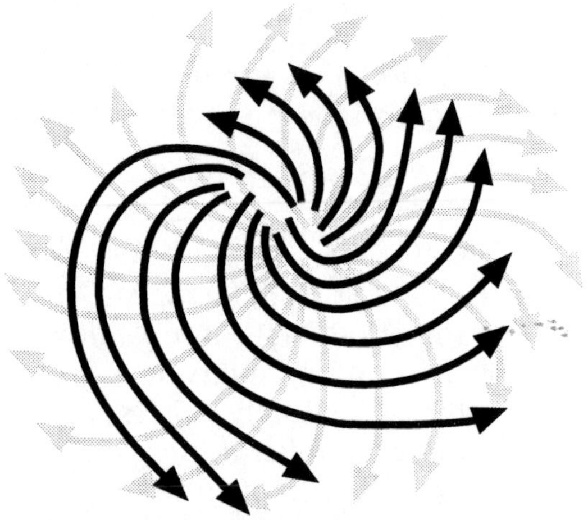

This curious pattern 1, 1, 2, 3, 5, 8, 13, 21, 34, 55, . . . is known to mathematicians by the name "The Fibonacci Sequence." The pattern is named after Leonardo Fibonacci, who discovered it when he was studying rabbits about 800 years ago.

Further Explorations

1. If you are interested in learning more about the Fibonacci sequence, look for the subject "Golden Ratio" in your library.
2. You may also examine a pineapple. Stick a marker such as a pencil in one of the scales at the bottom of the pineapple to help you keep track of your counts. Count all the diagonals of scales that go all the way around the pineapple as you move up and to the right ↗. How many did you get? Now return to your marker. This time count all the diagonals of scales around the pineapple as you move up and the left ↖. How many did you get? When we did this experiment, we got 8 spirals in one direction and 13 in the other. $^8/_{13}$ is another Fibonacci ratio.

Kinds of Fractions

When the numerator of a fraction is smaller than the denominator, such as $\frac{1}{2}$ or $\frac{2}{3}$ or $\frac{5}{6}$, the value of the fraction is less than 1. Such fractions are called **proper** fractions.

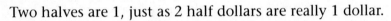

$\frac{1}{2}$ $\frac{2}{3}$ $\frac{5}{6}$

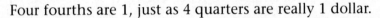

Fractions whose numerators are equal to their denominators, such as $\frac{2}{2}$ or $\frac{4}{4}$, and fractions whose numerators are larger than their denominators, such as $\frac{7}{4}$ or $\frac{3}{2}$, are called **improper** fractions.

Question: What is the value of a fraction whose numerator and denominator are equal?

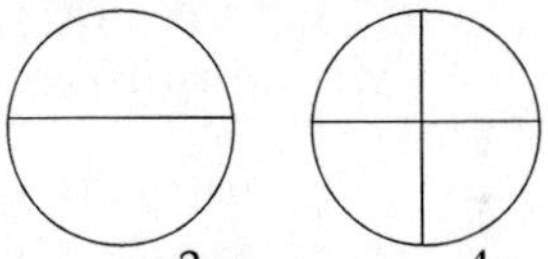

$\frac{2}{2}$ $\frac{4}{4}$

Two halves are 1, just as 2 half dollars are really 1 dollar.

Four fourths are 1, just as 4 quarters are really 1 dollar.

Do you see that a fraction whose numerator and denominator are exactly alike really has the value of 1? This is always true, whether the fraction is $\frac{4}{4}$ or $\frac{555}{555}$ or $\frac{2\text{ days}}{2\text{ days}}$. The only exception is $\frac{0}{0}$, which has no meaning.

Improper Fractions and Mixed Numbers

Until now, the fractions we have practiced writing have had numerators which were less than their denominators. Now let's look at fractions whose numerators are bigger than their denominators—like $\frac{5}{4}$ and $\frac{12}{6}$.

Those fractions are "overloaded." There is more in them than can fit into one. Twelve sixths ($\frac{12}{6}$) is like trying to get 12 people into a very small car—a car that's built for 6 people. Can you imagine the extra people hanging onto the hood and sitting on the roof? If you were smart, you'd get another car.

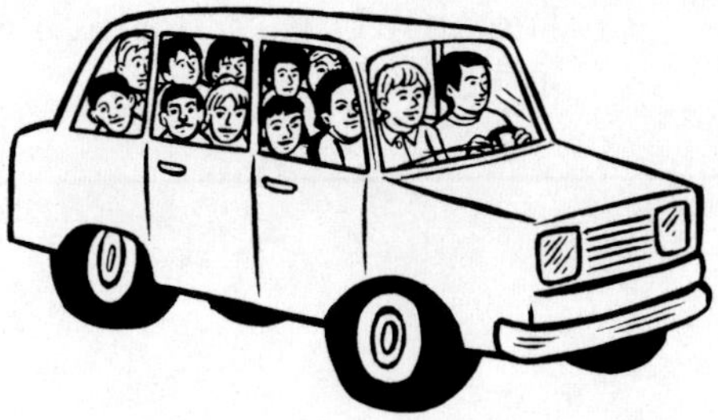

Name ______________________________

Date ______________________________

Reproducible

Take a look at $^{12}/_{6}$. How many cars built for 6 passengers would you need to hold 12? 2. Therefore—$^{12}/_{6}$ must be the same as 2.

Now, take a look at $^{5}/_{4}$. Think of 5 quarters.

That's the same as one dollar and one quarter left over, or $1\,^{1}/_{4}$.

One and one-fourth is called a **mixed number**, because it's a mixture of a whole number and a fraction. It should be thought of as a single number.

You can see that a mixed number is a whole number plus a bit left over: a **remainder**. You don't have quite enough to reach the next whole number.

Look again at those fractions: $^{12}/_{6}$ and $^{5}/_{4}$

We said $^{12}/_{6} = 2$. How did we get that answer? Well, $12 \div 6 = 2$.

We also said that $^{5}/_{4} = 1\,^{1}/_{4}$. How did we get that? Same way.

A Handy Rule for Changing Improper Fractions into Whole Numbers or Mixed Numbers

To change an improper fraction into a whole number or a mixed number, divide the denominator into the numerator. If there is a remainder, write it over the divisor.

More examples:	$^{28}/_{7} = 7\overline{)28}$ with quotient 4	There is no remainder, so the answer is just the whole number 4.
	$^{30}/_{7} = 7\overline{)30}$ with quotient 4; $\underline{28}$; 2	There is a remainder, so write 4, then $^{2}/_{7}$. The answer is $4\,^{2}/_{7}$, which we read as "4 and two sevenths."

Word Problems for Practice (V)

1. In the following paragraph, identify the improper fraction. Put a circle around it.
   The Fingerhut Sewing Shop had strips of cloth scattered over its shelves. The red cloth was $^{3}/_{4}$ meter long, the blue cloth $^{19}/_{5}$ meters long, the green cloth $^{9}/_{10}$ meter long, and the yellow cloth $^{32}/_{37}$ meter long.
2. Snoopy, the family dog, weighs 21 and seven-eighths pounds. Write Snoopy's weight as a mixed number. __________
3. The City College basketball team had beaten Wilson State College 19 times and lost to them 4 times over several years. Write the ratio of City College's wins to their losses. Express this improper fraction as a mixed number.
   ____
4. One year there were 55 Democrats in the United States Senate and 45 Republicans. Write the ratio of Democrats to Republicans. Write this improper fraction as a mixed number. __________
5. Alex had a part-time job working in a video rental store. He worked 4 days each week. Write the ratio of numbers of days he worked each week to the number of days he did not work __________. Express the result as a mixed number __________.
6. In the arcade at the Mall there are pinball machines. If you play a pinball machine and get a high score, you win a free game. (You get to play without having to put another quarter into the slot.) And the higher you score, the more free games you win.

   Two boys and two girls were playing machines. George won 17 free games while putting 5 quarters into the machine. Joe won 6 free games while putting 10 quarters into the machine. Sally won 23 free games while putting 2 quarters into the machine. Mitzi won 1 free game while putting 23 quarters into the machine. For each person, write the ratio of games won to quarters used in the blanks below.

   George ______________ Sally ______________
   Joe ______________ Mitzi ______________

   Which are improper fractions? ______________
   Change these to mixed numbers.
   Sometimes it is necessary to change mixed numbers into improper fractions. How do we do this?
   Go back to the example of $1\,^{1}/_{4}$. That's one dollar and one quarter, or 5 quarters altogether: $1\,^{1}/_{4} = {}^{5}/_{4}$
   Have you discovered a rule?

Name ______________________________
Date ______________________________

A Handy Rule for Changing Mixed Numbers into Improper Fractions

To change a **mixed number** into an improper fraction, first multiply the whole number by the denominator. Then add the numerator of the given fraction to this result. Write this sum over the denominator.

Example:	To change $1\frac{1}{4}$ into an improper fraction, first multiply $1 \times 4 = 4$. Then add $4 + 1 = 5$. Finally, write $\frac{5}{4}$.

Drill for Skill (I)

1. Write each of the following as a whole number:

   $\frac{8}{2}$ = ________ $\frac{6}{3}$ = ________ $\frac{50}{25}$ = ________ $\frac{75}{3}$ = ________

2. Write each of the following as a mixed number:

   $\frac{8}{3}$ = ________ $\frac{6}{5}$ = ________ $\frac{51}{25}$ = ________ $\frac{73}{3}$ = ________

3. Write each of these mixed numbers as an improper fraction:

   $1\frac{4}{5}$ = ________ $2\frac{9}{10}$ = ________ $3\frac{5}{6}$ = ________ $29\frac{1}{7}$ = ________

Reducing Fractions to Lower Terms

Reducing fractions makes them easier to handle. Suppose someone gave you 50 pennies. As a fractional part of a dollar, you know that 50 pennies are equal to $\frac{50}{100}$. But 50 pennies are a nuisance to carry around and $\frac{50}{100}$ is a rather awkward fraction. Especially when you know that 50 pennies are exactly the same as a half-dollar coin, so $\frac{50}{100}$ must be exactly the same as $\frac{1}{2}$. Changing the more awkward fraction $\frac{50}{100}$ to $\frac{1}{2}$ makes the fractions look different; but they still have the same value. For example, from our previous discussion, you know that $\frac{2}{2}$ $\frac{4}{4}$ $\frac{5}{5}$ $\frac{6}{6}$ $\frac{7}{7}$ are all equal to 1. Can you think of other examples of fractions which look different, but have the same value? What about $\frac{1}{2}$ and $\frac{2}{4}$? Or $\frac{3}{6}$?

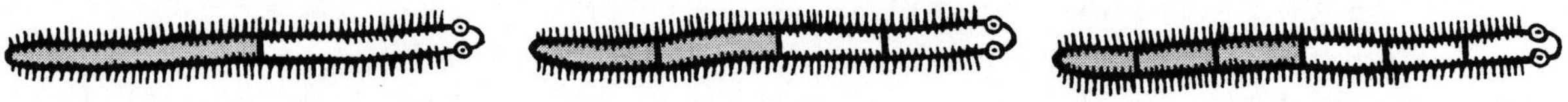

The Fundamental Rule for Fractions

This rule says that when we **multiply** or **divide** both the **numerator** and **denominator** of a fraction by the **same** number, the value of the fraction does not change. This rule holds for multiplying or dividing by any number except zero.

Example:	Take $1/2$, for instance. If we multiply both numerator and denominator by 2, we get $\frac{1 \times 2}{2 \times 2} = 2/4$. If we multiply both numerator and denominator by 3, we get $\frac{1 \times 3}{2 \times 3} = 3/6$.

Now, we will draw on the part of this fundamental rule involving division to show you how to reduce fractions. Look at the fractions above. Divide both the numerator and denominator by the same number. This process is called **reducing the fraction to lower terms**.

$2/4 = \frac{2 \div 2}{4 \div 2} = 1/2$.

$3/6 = \frac{3 \div 3}{6 \div 3} = 1/2$.

You will notice that in these examples, all the divisions were exact; there were no remainders.

When the terms of a fraction have been reduced so much that no whole number bigger than 1 will divide both the numerator and denominator exactly, the fraction is in **lowest terms**.

$1/2$ is in lowest terms, because no whole number bigger than 1 will divide both 1 and 2 exactly.

$2/3$ is in lowest terms.

$2/4$ is **not** in lowest terms, because we can divide both numerator and denominator by 2.

$8/12$ is **not** in lowest terms. Why? We can divide both the numerator and denominator by 2. Then we get $4/6$. Still not lowest terms. How about $2/3$?

Some Hints That May Help You to Reduce Fractions

	2 divides a number if 2 divides its last digit.
Example:	2 divides 378, because 2 divides 8 exactly 4 times.
	3 divides a number if 3 divides the sum of its digits.
Example:	3 divides 378, because 3 + 7 + 8 = 18, and 3 divides 18 exactly 6 times.
	4 divides a number if 4 divides the number formed by its last 2 digits.
Example:	4 divides 380, because 4 divides 80 exactly 20 times.
	5 divides a number if the number ends in 0 or 5.
	9 divides a number if 9 divides the sum of its digits.
Example:	9 divides 10098, because 1 + 0 + 0 + 9 + 8 = 18, and 9 divides 18 exactly 2 times.
	10 divides a number if the number ends in 0.

Drill for Skill (II)

1. Multiply the numerator and denominator of each fraction by 2:

   a. $\frac{1}{5}$ = __________ c. $\frac{3}{10}$ = __________ e. $\frac{5}{6}$ = __________

   b. $\frac{2}{5}$ = __________ d. $\frac{4}{3}$ = __________ f. $\frac{7}{8}$ = __________

2. Reduce each fraction to lowest terms:

   a. $\frac{6}{8}$ = __________ c. $\frac{9}{12}$ = __________ e. $\frac{75}{100}$ = __________

   b. $\frac{10}{15}$ = __________ d. $\frac{50}{100}$ = __________ f. $\frac{12}{100}$ = __________

3. At birth, an elephant weighed 200 pounds. When the elephant became an adult, he weighed 10,000 pounds. Write the ratio of the elephant's weight at birth to its adult weight. Reduce this ratio to lowest terms. ___________

4. Challenge Problem: A helicopter reporting rush-hour traffic for a local station flew over the suburbs. The helicopter flew at an altitude of 1,340 feet. There are 5,280 feet in a mile. What fractional part of a mile is 1,340 feet? Reduce this ratio to lowest terms. ___________

Some History About Fractions

Some of the ideas about using fractions date back to ancient times. However, it took a long time for people to develop a way of writing fractions, so that they would be able to add, subtract, multiply and divide with these numbers.

Around 1100 B.C., the Chinese used ideas relating to fractions in commerce. Early Egyptians and Babylonians used ideas relating to fractions in measurement and in trade. Ancient Roman laws of inheritance used ideas relating to fractions in dividing up estates.

Early symbols for writing fractions were much different from the symbols we use today. An early Greek symbol for $\frac{1}{2}$ was a measuring vessel cut in half. It looked something like this  . An early Egyptian symbol for $\frac{1}{4}$ was the cross with four arms, *X*.

In ancient times, Babylonians only used a denominator of 60; Romans used only a denominator of 12. Before 1800 B.C., the Egyptians and Greeks used only "unit fractions" (fractions which had a numerator of 1).

You can see that the ability of ancient people to use fractions was much more limited than it is today. In the unit fraction system, all fractions were expressed as the sum of fractions with a numerator of 1. Fractions whose numerators were greater than 1 probably arose in Babylon. The Arabs probably introduced the idea of writing the bar between the numerator and denominator of a fraction in the twelfth century. As far as we know, the word "fraction" was first used by the famous English poet Geoffrey Chaucer in the 1300's. In English literature before that time, fractions were referred to as "broken numbers."

Adding and Subtracting Fractions

Teacher Notes

+

Chapter 2 begins with adding fractions with the same denominator. It discusses the various terms students might find in word problems that indicate addition, such as *altogether, combined, together,* and *in all.* Students are also alerted that sometimes such words don't actually appear in the problem but must be inferred. Next comes subtraction of fractions with like denominators. As with addition problems, there is discussion of terms in word problems that are signals to subtract, such as *how much is left?, how much shorter?, what is the difference?,* and *how much remained?*

Answers

Handy Rule (Addition) Problems
a. $2/3$ b. $8/9$ c. $5/6$ d. $17/20$

Word Problems for Practice VI
1. $1/2$ mi., **2.** $4/5$ acre, **3.** $3/5$ lb., **4.** $3/16$ in., **5.** $3/4$ hr.

Word Problems for Practice VII
1. $1\,1/4$ gal., **2.** $7/25$, **3.** $5/6$, **4.** $3/5$, **5.** $2/5$, **6.** $1/2$, **7.** $3/5$, **8.** $3/8$. **A Piece of the Action:** $1\,1/5$; yes

Handy Rule (Subtraction) Problems
a. $2/3$ b. $1/4$ c. $1/3$ d. $13/24$

Word Problems for Practice VIII
1. $1/4$ hr., **2.** $2/5$ min., **3.** $11/24$ in., **4.** $21/25$ sec., **5.** $3/16$ in., **6.** $1/2$ *l*

Word Problems for Practice IX
1. $1/4$ bottle, **2.** $2/5$ hr., **3.** $3/5$ *l*, **4.** $1/2$ c., **5.** $1/32$ in., **6.** $1/2$ ton. **The Body Builders:** upper arm: $7/8$ in., lower leg: $3/4$ in., upper leg: $5/8$ in.

Name ______________________________

Date ______________________________

Reproducible

Adding and Subtracting Fractions

Let's talk about adding and subtracting fractions. First, let's talk about **quarters**.

What is $\frac{1}{4} + \frac{1}{4}$?

Well, what is  +  ?

Fifty cents, or **one-half** dollar. You could also say it's **two quarters**.

So $\frac{1}{4} + \frac{1}{4}$ = two quarters or $\frac{2}{4}$ or $\frac{1}{2}$.

Now, add another quarter:  +  + 

That's 75 cents or **three quarters**. $\frac{1}{4} + \frac{1}{4} + \frac{1}{4} = \frac{3}{4}$

Add another quarter:  +  +  +  =

four quarters, or $1

So $\frac{1}{4} + \frac{1}{4} + \frac{1}{4} + \frac{1}{4} = \frac{4}{4}$ or 1: a whole.

"Stop!" You may say. "I can see that two quarters make half a dollar. So I guess $\frac{1}{4} + \frac{1}{4}$ must be a half. But I would have guessed that in adding fractions you would add 1 and 1 on the top, which gives you 2; and 4 and 4 on the bottom, which gives you 8. That would give you $\frac{2}{8}$."

"That sure would give you $\frac{2}{8}$," your teacher might say. "But we know already that 2 quarters make a half. So your method of adding fractions **must be wrong**."

"I guess so. What do you do?"

"Take another look. How can you make $\frac{1}{4} + \frac{1}{4} = \frac{2}{4}$?"

"Let me think. Don't rush me. H'm. I got it. Just add the top numbers and forget about the bottom. Leave it as is."

"Good. You got it!"

Name ______________________________

Date ______________________________

A Handy Rule for Adding Fractions Whose Denominators Are the Same

Here is the rule for adding fractions with the same denominator. When the denominators of two or more fractions are the same, just add the numerators. Put that sum over whatever the denominator is. That is your answer.

Example:	$\frac{1}{4}+\frac{1}{4}=\frac{2}{4}$	$\frac{3}{6}+\frac{1}{6}=\frac{4}{6}$	$\frac{9}{10}+\frac{2}{10}+\frac{1}{10}=\frac{12}{10}=1\frac{2}{10}=1\frac{1}{5}$

Try these.

(a) $\frac{1}{3}+\frac{1}{3}=$ ________

(b) $\frac{5}{9}+\frac{1}{9}+\frac{2}{9}=$ ________

(c) $\frac{2}{6}+\frac{3}{6}=$ ________

(d) $\frac{1}{20}+\frac{6}{20}+\frac{10}{20}=$ ________

Word problems that call for the use of addition usually ask you to **accumulate** things. The basic idea of addition is to **join** things, to put things together. When the problem requires that you do this, addition is your tool. Problems which involve addition often use **key words** such as

altogether
in all
total
combined
sum

These key words are very important signals that addition is required, so be on the lookout for them.

Let's try a problem.

Andy and Robert were collecting old newspapers to sell. Andy's pile of papers weighed $\frac{1}{16}$ of a ton. Robert's weighed $\frac{3}{16}$ of a ton. How much did the papers weigh in all?

In reading the problem, you can see you are asked to put together what Andy and Robert have collected. This indicates addition. And there at the very end of the problem are the key words **in all**. So, now you know you must add to solve the problem.

Your next step is to take your numbers out of the paragraph. The numbers are $\frac{1}{16}$ and $\frac{3}{16}$.

Now, examine the numbers. You can see they are fractions with the same denominator. You can use the method of adding fractions you have just learned.

Remember, when we have fractions with like denominators, we simply add the numerators, putting that sum over the denominator. So $^1/_{16} + {^3/_{16}} = {^4/_{16}}$. Our answer then is $^4/_{16}$. Reduce this to lowest terms and you have $^1/_4$. Since the problem is talking about tons, we must use this unit of measure in our answer. So, the answer is $^1/_4$ ton.

Word Problems for Practice (VI)

Now go ahead and solve the following problems using the same approach. Look at what the problem is asking you to do and underline any key words indicating addition. Reduce your answers to lowest terms.

1. Every morning Beth walks $^1/_4$ mile to school. In the late afternoon, she returns home walking another $^1/_4$ mile. What is her total walk each day going to and from school?

   ____

2. Two sisters each owned $^2/_5$ acre of valuable city land. Their tracts of land were next to each other. If the sisters pooled their land, how large would the combined tract of land be?

   ____

3. Two friends were walking along the boardwalk at the beach and enjoying the sun and the view. They each bought $^3/_{10}$ lb. of salt water taffy. How much taffy did they buy in all?

   ____

4. Lisa bought a new pair of blue jeans. She tried them on, looked in the mirror and felt the jeans did not fit as closely as she wanted. She decided to shrink the jeans. She soaked them twice. The first time the jeans shrank $^2/_{16}$ of an inch. The second time the jeans shrank another $^1/_{16}$ of an inch from the original size. How much did she shrink the jeans in all?

   ____

5. Julie went to a party at her girlfriend's house, where she saw many of her friends and spent some time dancing. She danced with Gary for $^1/_4$ hour, with Bob for $^1/_4$ hour and with Gil for $^1/_4$ hour. How much time did she spend dancing altogether?

   ____

Name ____________________

Date ____________________

+

Reproducible

More About Addition Word Problems

In some word problems which involve addition, these key words do not actually appear. However, the logic of the problem requires **accumulating** or **joining**. If this is the case, the problems may be written as if the key words were actually there without changing the meaning of the problem.

Example:	A box turtle was taking a leisurely stroll through the forest. In the first hour it walked $\frac{3}{100}$ kilometer. In the second hour, it walked $\frac{6}{100}$ kilometer. How far did the turtle walk during the two hours? ____________
Solution:	The problem calls for accumulating the distances. The problem could be restated by changing the last line to, "How far did the turtle walk **altogether? Altogether** is a key word indicating that we must **add**.
	$\frac{3}{100}$ kilometer + $\frac{6}{100}$ kilometer = $\frac{9}{100}$ kilometer
Answer:	$\frac{9}{100}$ kilometer

Word Problems for Practice (VII)

Study the following problems. Look for what each problem asks you to do. Does it ask for accumulating or joining? If so, then restate the problem to yourself using one of the key words for addition. Work the problem. Reduce all answers to lowest terms.

1. There were two large plastic bottles of milk in the refrigerator. One bottle contained $\frac{3}{4}$ gallon of milk while the other contained $\frac{2}{4}$ gallon of milk. How much milk was there in the refrigerator? ____________

2. The Fitzby Lumber Yard had fallen on hard times. Four twenty-fifths of its lumber supply had been damaged by fire. Another $\frac{1}{25}$ had been damaged by a band of hungry termites. Finally, $\frac{2}{25}$ of the lumber had been damaged by flooding. What part of the total supply of lumber had been damaged?

   ____

3. Ben was looking over his school grades for the last three years. One sixth of the grades were A's, $\frac{2}{6}$ were B's, $\frac{2}{6}$ were C's, and $\frac{1}{6}$ were D's. What part of his grades were C or better? ____________

4. An investment company put $\frac{4}{10}$ of its money into stocks and $\frac{2}{10}$ into bonds. The rest of its money was kept in the bank in reserve. What part of the company's money was invested in stocks and bonds? ____________

5. On first down, a football team ran a running play which took $\frac{3}{10}$ minute. On second down, they ran a passing play which took $\frac{1}{10}$ minute. How much time did the team use on the two downs? ____________

6. Ruth and Grace were giving a party. One sixth of the guests they invited came from Ruth's school and two sixths of the guests came from Grace's school. The rest of the guests were relatives and neighbors. What fraction of the guests were school friends of the girls? ____________

7. Jefferson Junior High conducted a survey to find out how many students used their seat belts when riding in their parents' cars. One fifth of the students said that they always used their seat belts. Two fifths said they sometimes used their seat belts. What fraction of the students surveyed said they used their seat belts at least some of the time? ____________

8. A group of students met at the state university to share experiences. One eighth of the students came from Africa; one eight came from Asia; and one eighth came from Latin America. What fraction of the students in the group came from these foreign lands? ____________

A Piece of the Action

Mugsey Brown had to be the world's worst prize fighter. He was simply awful. Some fighters are super quick; Mugsey was just the opposite. In the ring he moved like a hippopotamus and hit like a summer breeze. He had only one thing going for him. His jaw was like a rock. When a boxer hit him with a right cross, Mugsey only smiled. His opponent would walk away with a "busted" hand.

When word got around that Mugsey might be the next champ, the fight crowd wanted in on the action. People began to approach Mugsey's manager, asking whether they could buy a share of Mugsey's contract and become a partner in Mugsey's rise to the top. The manager was agreeable. A group in Chicago bought up $\frac{1}{5}$ of his contract. Then a steel company bought up another $\frac{1}{5}$ of the contract. They planned to advertise Mugsey's face on their steel bars. Slim Mackin, the former cowboy star, bought up $\frac{1}{5}$ of the contract. Finally an oil sheik from the Middle East purchased $\frac{3}{5}$ of the contract.

How much of Mugsey's contract was sold? ________

Was Mugsey's contract oversold? ________

You bet it was!

Subtracting Fractions Whose Denominators Are the Same

Now, let's talk about subtracting fractions. Remember that in adding fractions whose denominators are the same, we simply

(a) add the numerators;

(b) the denominators stay the **same**.

A Handy Rule for Subtracting Fractions with the Same Denominator

In subtracting fractions whose denominators are the same, we

(a) just subtract the numerators;

(b) the denominators stay the **same**.

Like this: $\frac{3}{4} - \frac{2}{4} = \frac{1}{4}$ or $\frac{8}{12} - \frac{3}{12} = \frac{5}{12}$ or $\frac{9}{16} - \frac{2}{16} = \frac{7}{16}$

Try these. Reduce all answers to lowest terms.

(a) $\frac{9}{12} - \frac{1}{12} =$ ________ (c) $\frac{5}{9} - \frac{2}{9} =$ ________

(b) $\frac{3}{4} - \frac{2}{4} =$ ________ (d) $\frac{16}{24} - \frac{3}{24} =$ ________

What about $\frac{9}{8} - \frac{9}{8} = \frac{0}{8}$? $\frac{0}{8}$? *Hmm . . .*

Think: I have something and I **take it all away**. $\frac{9}{8} - \frac{9}{8}$

If I take it away, I have **0**. So $\frac{9}{8} - \frac{9}{8} = 0$. Right!

Note: If a fraction's numerator is 0, and the fraction's denominator is 0, the value of the fraction is 0.

Word problems that ask you to find **differences** and to look for **what remains** almost always are asking you to **subtract**. The **differences** may be in time, length, area, or in almost any measure you can think of. For example, how do two pieces of wood differ in length? Sometimes difference problems are worded to look for changes, as in before and after measurements. For example, what is a person's weight loss after going on a diet program? Some illustrations of **what remains** are 1) what is left after you saw off a log or 2) what is left after you withdraw money from a bank account. When you see problems requiring you to find differences or what remains, think **subtraction**!

Name ____________________________

Date ____________________________

Example: After a heavy snowfall, a drift in front of a house was $\frac{2}{3}$ foot high. If after a day of sunshine, $\frac{1}{3}$ foot of the drift had melted, how much of the snow drift remained?

Solution:

This problem asks you to look for *what remained,* a clear signal that you have to subtract to solve the problem. Take out the numbers from the sentence. The numbers are $\frac{2}{3}$ and $\frac{1}{3}$. You can see that they are fractions with like denominators. So, we can apply the arithmetical method we have just practiced. Subtract the numerators, keep the denominators the same, and place the difference between the numerators over the denominator.

$\frac{2}{3} - \frac{1}{3} = \frac{1}{3}$ (The answer is already in lowest terms.)

To complete our answer, we need only place the unit of measurement described in the problem next to the figure we calculated. What is the unit of measurement? A **foot**. So our answer is $\frac{1}{3}$ foot of snow.

Word Problems for Practice (VIII)

Try the following problems. Study what the problem is asking you to do and look closely for key phrases. Reduce your answers to lowest terms.

1. When Shirley left home, she had $\frac{3}{4}$ hour before her class started. Her bus got tied up in a traffic jam for $\frac{2}{4}$ hour. How much time was left for her to get to class? __________

2. A beginning computer user was able to type a paragraph in $\frac{7}{10}$ minute. An experienced computer user could type the same paragraph in $\frac{3}{10}$ minute. What is the difference between these typing times? __________

3. In building a stereo system, Marcie drilled a hole into a board that was $\frac{17}{24}$ inch in diameter. She drilled a second hole that was $\frac{6}{24}$ inch in diameter. How much longer was the diameter of the first hole than the second? __________

4. In a psychological experiment, the professor was testing how fast his students could react. When a light flashed, the student was supposed to press a bar as fast as he or she could. The fastest student pressed the bar in $\frac{3}{25}$ of a second after the light had flashed; the slowest student, $\frac{24}{25}$ second after the light had flashed. What was the difference in reaction time between the fastest and slowest student? __________

5. The ice on the pond where everyone liked to skate during the winter was $\frac{15}{16}$ of an inch at its thickest point and $\frac{12}{16}$ of an inch at its thinnest point. What was the difference in the thickness of the ice for these two points?

   ____

6. Joe left $\frac{5}{6}$ liter of water sitting in the hot sun. Two sixths of a liter of this water evaporated. How much of the water remained? __________

More About Subtraction Word Problems

As was true for addition, key words or phrases are not always present in problems that require you to subtract. However, if you study the problems carefully you will find such ideas as **difference** and **what remains** are in the problems even when these words themselves are not used in the problem. When you find this happening, try restating the problem with one of the key phrases. you will see this will not change the meaning of the problem.

Example: Rae was able to swim the length of her apartment pool in $\frac{28}{30}$ minute. After much practice, she was able to swim this distance in $\frac{21}{30}$ minute. By how much had she reduced her swim time?

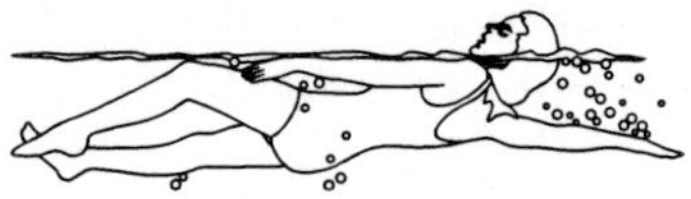

Solution: Rae had reduced her swim time by the **difference** between the swim times. Therefore the last line of the problem could be restated as "What was the difference between the swim times?"

$\frac{28}{30}$ minute – $\frac{21}{30}$ minute = $\frac{7}{30}$ minute

Word Problems for Practice (IX)

In each problem below, restate the problem using key words. Then work the problem. Reduce each answer to lowest terms.

1. The Anderson family was driving to the mountains. Mrs. Anderson filled $\frac{2}{4}$ of a thermos bottle with coffee to take along. She sipped the coffee and found it was too strong. To make it weaker, she added boiling water until the bottle was $\frac{3}{4}$ filled. How much water did she pour into the thermos bottle? ______________

2. If it takes $\frac{1}{5}$ hour to lubricate a car and $\frac{3}{5}$ hour to both lubricate the car and change the oil, how long would it take to only change the oil?

   ____

3. Mrs. Kim put $4/5$ liter of orange juice on the breakfast table. After her children had finished breakfast there was only $1/5$ liter in the bottle. How much orange juice had been consumed? ____________

4. A recipe for a low-calorie dish called for $3/4$ cup of skim milk. The cook had only $1/4$ cup of skim milk. How much more milk did the cook need?

   ____

5. A draftsman was supposed to draw a line exactly $25/32$ inch long. However, he made an error and drew the line $26/32$ inch. What was the size of his error? ____________

6. Two robots were built to lift heavy weights. The first robot was able to lift $1/6$ ton of steel. The second robot was above to lift $4/6$ ton of steel. How much more steel could the second robot lift than the first? ____________

The Body Builders

Benjie and Hermie were dressed in their gym suits and looked in the mirror. They both looked flabby and out of shape. Benjie said to Hermie, "You look like the 97-pound weakling I saw in the magazine ad—the one who always gets sand kicked in his face." Hermie turned around and replied. "Well, Benjie, you ain't exactly Mr. Universe." After a pushing and shoving match in which neither had strength enough to do any damage to the other, they decided to write for Mr. Muscles' *Body Building Book.* For 3 months, they trained like mad; they did pushups and situps as well as all the exercises recommended by Mr. Muscles. Then they took measurements to see who had improved most.

Hermie had increased his upper arm muscles (biceps) by $15/16$" while Benjie had increased his upper arm muscles by $1/16$".

Hermie had increased his lower leg muscles (calves) by $14/16$" while Benjie had increased his lower leg muscles by $2/16$".

Hermie had increased his upper leg muscles (thighs) by $13/16$" while Benjie had increased his upper leg muscles by $3/16$".

Calculate the difference between Benjie's and Hermie's gains in muscle size for each set of muscles.

Upper arm muscles ____________ Lower leg muscles ____________

Upper leg muscles ____________

(Benjie was so impressed by Hermie's muscular development that he sent Hermie's picture to Mr. Muscles himself. Mr. Muscles put Hermie's picture on his ads beside his own picture. Now you can see the two of them standing side by side flexing their muscles—Mr. Muscles and Mr. Muscles, Jr.)

" means inches

Addition and Subtraction of Fractions with Unlike Denominators

Teacher Notes

The chapter begins with the need for common denominators—illustrated by the pitfall of simply adding unlike denominators—and then uses a word problem to show students how to find them. The discussion then moves on to finding the least common denominator. It gives Handy Rules for both these processes. Equivalent fractions are defined and illustrated. A short quiz on the rules of using common denominators helps clarify these principles for students before they are given a number of exercises that involve finding the lowest common denominator and then adding or subtracting to solve the problem itself.

Answers

Practice in Finding Common Denominators:

No. The lcd for $\frac{3}{8}$ and $\frac{1}{3}$ is 24.

Drill for Skill III

1. 12, **2.** 10, **3.** 20, **4.** 9

Drill for Skill IV

1. is done for students, **2.** 6, $\frac{3}{6}$, $\frac{2}{6}$, **3.** 30, $\frac{6}{30}$, $\frac{10}{30}$, **4.** 42, $\frac{12}{42}$, $\frac{7}{42}$, **5.** 10, $\frac{8}{10}$, $\frac{3}{10}$, **6.** 12, $\frac{2}{12}$, $\frac{3}{12}$, **7.** 56, $\frac{21}{56}$, $\frac{32}{56}$

Quiz Yourself

1. $\frac{1}{2}$ is smaller, **2.** $\frac{8}{5}$ is larger, **3.** $\frac{7}{8}$ and $\frac{14}{16}$ are equal

Drill for Skill V

1. $1\frac{1}{12}$, **2.** $\frac{5}{6}$, **3.** $\frac{2}{3}$, **4.** 2, **5.** $1\frac{1}{88}$, **6.** $\frac{5}{6}$, **7.** 1

A Short Quiz on the Rules

1. never, **2.** when the denominators are the same and we are adding, **3.** never, **4.** When the denominators are the same and we are subtracting

Drill for Skill VI

1. $\frac{1}{9}$, **2.** $\frac{1}{4}$, **3.** $\frac{3}{16}$, **4.** $\frac{1}{3}$, **5.** $\frac{5}{16}$, **6.** $1\frac{11}{12}$.

Word Problems for Practice X

1. $1\frac{1}{4}$ hrs., **2.** $2\frac{1}{6}$ lbs., **3.** $2\frac{1}{24}$ min., **4.** $\frac{3}{4}$ measure, **5.** $\frac{13}{15}$ of the vote, **6.** $\frac{11}{12}$ hr., **7.** $\frac{9}{16}$ of the stamps, **8.** $\frac{5}{6}$ of their vacation, **9.** $\frac{17}{24}$ of total income, **10.** $\frac{9}{20}$ mi. **Making Movies:** $1\frac{1}{2}$ km

Word Problems for Practice XI

1. $\frac{13}{24}$ horsepower, **2.** $\frac{3}{10}$ hr., **3.** $\frac{1}{4}$ in., **4.** by $\frac{1}{10}$, **5.** $\frac{1}{12}$ karat, **6.** **(a)** Bill **(b)** $\frac{1}{24}$, **7.** $\frac{11}{60}$ in., **8.** second book, $\frac{1}{16}$ in., **9.** $\frac{13}{24}$ m, **10.** $\frac{3}{8}$ g.

Name ______________________________

Date ______________________________

Reproducible

Addition and Subtraction of Fractions That Have Unlike Denominators

We have now finished our study of word problems that ask you to add or subtract fractions whose denominators are the same. But things are not always so easy. You will often have to solve addition and subtraction problems where the denominators are not the same. In this section we will show you how to add and subtract fractions whose denominators are unlike.

To get started, let's go back to our very first addition problem—the one about the two boys collecting newspapers. Remember this?

Andy and Robert were collecting old newspapers to sell. Andy's pile of papers weighed $\frac{1}{16}$ of a ton. Robert's weighed $\frac{3}{16}$ of a ton. How much did the papers weigh in all?

You can see that both of the denominators for this problem are the same: 16. You know how to add fractions like these. But what would you do if the figures were $\frac{1}{3}$ and $\frac{1}{4}$ instead of $\frac{1}{16}$ and $\frac{3}{16}$. How would you do that?

In thinking about the problem, you might be tempted to say something like this:

$\frac{1}{3} + \frac{1}{4}$. Just add the numerators—you get 2. Add the denominators, you get 7. The answer is $\frac{2}{7}$. Right?

Wrong.

If it isn't $\frac{2}{7}$, what is it? How do you add fractions with unlike denominators?

You must start by finding a **common denominator**.

Name ______________________

Date ______________________

Reproducible

Addition and Subtraction of Fractions with Unlike Denominators

Common Denominators

What is a **common denominator**? It is something that both things fit into equally well. For example, suppose someone asked you to think of a broader category that both men and women could fit into. How about "people," or "human beings"? Or what if someone asked you what category oranges, apples, and pears fit into. You might say, "Fruit." Or how about churches, apartments, and schools? Try buildings. In each case (people, fruit, buildings) are common denominators for the individual things.

Now let's take **numbers**. What number will both 3 and 4 go into exactly? Let's try 6: 3 will go into 6 two times. That's fine, but 4 won't go exactly into 6—there's a remainder. That's no good. In finding a common denominator, your numbers must divide the common denominator **exactly**. There can be nothing, and we mean **nothing**, left over. O.K.?

Let's try again. What number will both 3 and 4 divide into exactly? Let's try 8: 4 will go into 8 two times. That's fine, but 3 won't go into 8 exactly. Not so easy, is it? Well, let's try once more. What will 3 and 4 go into? Ah ha! They both go into 12 exactly. (4 goes into 12, 3 times; 3 goes into 12, 4 times.) **Twelve**, then, is a common denominator for 3 and 4.

If you think about it, you will discover other numbers that both 3 and 4 go into exactly. For example, 24 or 36 or 48. But, try as you may, you won't find a smaller or lower common denominator for these numbers than 12. And that's what we mean by the **least common denominator**. The **least common denominator** is the smallest whole number larger than zero that all of our denominators will go into exactly.

SOME DEFINITIONS:	Remember . . . When we have fractions, "common denominators" for our fractions are whole numbers larger than 0 that all of our denominators divide exactly. "The least common denominator" of our fractions is the smallest number in the list of their common denominators.

Name ______________________________

Date ______________________________

Reproducible

Addition and Subtraction of Fractions with Unlike Denominators

A Handy Rule for Finding a Common Denominator

If you are having trouble finding "any" common denominator—and much more trouble finding the least common denominator—you can always find a common denominator by multiplying your denominators together.

This product will always be a common denominator; however, it might not be the least common denominator. For example, a common denominator for $\frac{1}{5}$ and $\frac{1}{8}$ is $5 \times 8 = 40$. A common denominator $\frac{2}{7}$ and $\frac{4}{9}$ is 63. A common denominator for $\frac{1}{12}$ and $\frac{2}{9}$ is $12 \times 9 = 108$. However, 108 is not the least common denominator for $\frac{1}{12}$ and $\frac{2}{9}$.

A Handy Rule for Finding the Least Common Denominator

1. Look at each fraction. For each fraction, make a list of whole numbers larger than 0 that each denominator will divide exactly.
2. The smallest number which is in both of these lists will be a least common denominator for your fractions.

Let's suppose that we want to find the least common denominator for the fractions $\frac{1}{12}$ and $\frac{2}{9}$. Our denominators are 12 and 9.

The list of whole numbers larger than 0 that 12 will divide exactly are

$12 \times 1 = 12$	$12 \times 2 = 24$	$12 \times 3 = 36$	$12 \times 4 = 48$
$12 \times 5 = 60$	$12 \times 6 = 72$	$12 \times 7 = 84$	$12 \times 9 = 108$, etc.

The list of whole numbers larger than 0 that 9 will divide exactly are

$9 \times 1 = 9$	$9 \times 2 = 18$	$9 \times 3 = 27$	$9 \times 4 = 36$
$9 \times 5 = 45$	$9 \times 6 = 54$	$9 \times 7 = 63$	$9 \times 8 = 72$
$9 \times 9 = 81$	$9 \times 10 = 90$	$9 \times 11 = 99$	$9 \times 12 = 108$, etc.

Let's write our lists of products.

(12, 24, 36, 48, 60, 72, 84, 108, . . .)

(9, 18, 27, 36, 45, 63, 72, 81, 90, 99, 108, . . .)

What is the smallest number that appears in both of these lists? __________

The least common denominator for our fractions $\frac{1}{12}$ and $\frac{2}{9}$ is 36.

Name ______________________________

Date ______________________________

Practice in Finding Common Denominators

Try finding a common denominator for $\frac{3}{8}$ and $\frac{1}{3}$.

Try to think of whole numbers larger than 0 that both 8 and 3 will "go into" exactly. If you can't think of anything, remember the handy rule for finding a common denominator: Multiply the two denominators. That gives 24. Is there a smaller common denominator?

Try finding a common denominator for $\frac{9}{16}$ and $\frac{1}{4}$.

If we use the handy rule for finding a common denominator and multiply 16×4, we get 64. This is a common denominator; but you can find smaller common denominators if you look for them. Did you say 32? Right. But, there is still a smaller common denominator. How about 16? 16 divides 16 exactly 1 time and 4 divides 16 exactly 4 times.

Drill for Skill (III)

Try to find the least common denominator for each pair of fractions below.

1. $\frac{8}{12}$ and $\frac{3}{4}$ ______________
2. $\frac{9}{10}$ and $\frac{1}{5}$ ______________
3. $\frac{1}{4}$ and $\frac{2}{5}$ ______________
4. $\frac{6}{9}$ and $\frac{1}{3}$ ______________

Now look at each common denominator you have found. Have you found the **least common denominator** for each of the given pairs of fractions?

Now that you know how to find common denominators, how can you use them to add (or for that matter to subtract) fractions whose denominators are not alike?

Let's take the fractions from our problem with the newspapers weighing $\frac{1}{3}$ ton + $\frac{1}{4}$ ton. We know that a common denominator for $\frac{1}{3}$ and $\frac{1}{4}$ is 12. Our goal is to change both $\frac{1}{3}$ into $\frac{?}{12}$ and $\frac{1}{4}$ into $\frac{?}{12}$.

Then we will do our adding easily, because both denominators will be the same. How do we make these changes into twelfths? Let's use some pictures to show how this can come about.

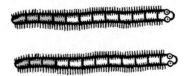

Look at the top pictures first. You can see that $\frac{1}{3}$ covers exactly the same amount of space that $\frac{4}{12}$ covers. $\frac{1}{3}$ and $\frac{4}{12}$ look like different fractions, but they have the same value. $\frac{1}{3}$ and $\frac{4}{12}$ are **equal** or **equivalent** fractions. The fractions look different but have the same value.

As not everyone can draw pictures that carefully, we will show you how to change both 1⁄3 and 1⁄4 into twelfths without drawing pictures. Here's what you do.

A Handy Rule for Finding an Equivalent Fraction

To change a given fraction into an equivalent fraction which has a different denominator, follow these steps:

1. First, divide the bottom of your fraction into the denominator you want.
2. Then multiply **both** the top and the bottom of your fraction by the answer you got in Step 1.

Example: $\frac{1}{3} = \frac{?}{12}$. Step 1. 3 into 12 is 4 Step 2. $\frac{1}{3} \times \frac{4}{4} = \frac{4}{12}$	Example: $\frac{1}{4} = \frac{?}{12}$. Step 1. 4 into 12 is 3 Step 2. $\frac{1}{4} \times \frac{3}{3} = \frac{3}{12}$

JUST FOR MATH BUFFS?	Remember the Fundamental Rule for Fractions (page 21)? It told us that we could multiply **both** the top and bottom of a fraction by the same number (except zero) without changing the value of the fraction. In the example above, we really used that rule. In changing $\frac{1}{3}$ into $\frac{4}{12}$, we multiplied both the numerator 1 and the denominator 3 by 4. In changing $\frac{1}{4}$ into $\frac{3}{12}$, we multiplied both the numerator 1 and the denominator 4 by 3.

Drill for Skill (IV)

Find a common denominator for each pair of fractions. Then change each fraction in the pair into an equivalent fraction having the common denominator as its new denominator.

1. $\frac{6}{12}$ and $\frac{1}{3}$ common denominator is 12 $\frac{6}{12} = \frac{6}{12}$ $\frac{1}{3} = \frac{4}{12}$
2. $\frac{1}{2}$ and $\frac{2}{6}$ common denominator is _____ $\frac{1}{2}$ = _____ $\frac{2}{6}$ = _____
3. $\frac{6}{30}$ and $\frac{5}{15}$ common denominator is _____ $\frac{6}{30}$ = _____ $\frac{5}{15}$ = _____
4. $\frac{2}{7}$ and $\frac{1}{6}$ common denominator is _____ $\frac{2}{7}$ = _____ $\frac{1}{6}$ = _____
5. $\frac{4}{5}$ and $\frac{3}{10}$ common denominator is _____ $\frac{4}{5}$ = _____ $\frac{3}{10}$ = _____
6. $\frac{1}{6}$ and $\frac{1}{4}$ common denominator is _____ $\frac{1}{6}$ = _____ $\frac{1}{4}$ = _____
7. $\frac{3}{8}$ and $\frac{4}{7}$ common denominator is _____ $\frac{3}{8}$ = _____ $\frac{4}{7}$ = _____

Name ____________________________

Date ____________________________

Reproducible

Comparing the Sizes of Fractions

If you have two fractions with different denominators, you might ask whether the first fraction is less than the second fraction, or whether the two fractions are equal, or whether the first fraction is larger than the second fraction. (The symbol for less than is <. The symbol for equal to is, of course =. The symbol for larger than is >.) One way of answering this question is to first find a common denominator for the fractions. Then change each fraction into an equivalent fraction having that common denominator as its denominator. Finally, compare the sizes of the numerators.

Example:	To compare $\frac{2}{3}$ with $\frac{3}{4}$,
	$\frac{2}{3} = \frac{8}{12}$ and $\frac{3}{4} = \frac{9}{12}$.
	8 is less than 9; so, $\frac{2}{3} < \frac{3}{4}$.

QUIZ YOURSELF

1. Compare $\frac{1}{2}$ with $\frac{2}{3}$.
2. Compare $\frac{8}{5}$ with $\frac{3}{2}$.
3. Compare $\frac{7}{8}$ with $\frac{14}{16}$.

A Handy Rule for Adding Fractions with Different Denominators

1. First, find a common denominator.
2. Second, change each fraction into an equivalent fraction having the common denominator as its denominator.
3. Add the fractions whose denominators are now alike.

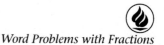

Name ______________________________

Date ______________________________

Reproducible

Addition and Subtraction of Fractions with Unlike Denominators

Let's take a practice problem.

$^3/_8 + ^1/_3$

Step 1. A **common denominator** is 24.
Step 2. Do you remember how to change $^3/_8$ and $^1/_3$ into 24ths?

$^3/_8 = ^?/_{24}$

a. Divide 8 into 24. Get 3.
b. Multiply top and bottom by 3:

$$\frac{3 \times 3}{8 \times 3} = \frac{9}{24}$$

$^1/_3 = ^?/_{24}$

a. Divide 3 into 24. Get 8.
b. Multiply top and bottom by 8:

$$\frac{1 \times 8}{3 \times 8} = \frac{8}{24}$$

Step 3. Now you can add fractions with like denominators. $^9/_{24} + ^8/_{24} = ^{17}/_{24}$.

Drill for Skill (V)

Try these:

1. $^1/_4 + ^5/_6 =$ __________
2. $^2/_4 + ^2/_6 =$ __________
3. $^2/_4 + ^1/_6 =$ __________
4. $^3/_2 + ^4/_8 =$ __________
5. $^7/_{11} + ^3/_8 =$ __________
6. $^1/_{12} + ^3/_4 =$ __________

BRAIN BUSTER! 7. $^1/_2 + ^1/_3 + ^1/_6 =$ __________

A Handy Rule for Subtracting Fractions with Different Denominators

1. First, find a common denominator.
2. Second, change each fraction into an equivalent fraction having the common denominator as its denominator.

   Subtract the equivalent fractions whose denominators are now alike.

   Now let's practice subtracting fractions whose denominators are different.

Let's take a practice problem.
$^9/_{16} - ^1/_4$
Step 1. What is a common denominator? 16.
Step 2. Change $^1/_4$ into $/_{16}$ths.
a. 4 into 16 is 4. b. $^1/_4 \times ^4/_4 = ^4/_{16}$
Step 3. $^9/_{16} - ^4/_{16} =$ Answer: $^5/_{16}$

Name ______________________________

Date ______________________________

You might be thinking . . . "When I subtract $\frac{9}{16} - \frac{1}{4}$, the instructions used the least common denominator 16. Another common denominator is 64, but it is not the least common denominator. What if I had used 64 as a common denominator instead of 16?"

Well, $\frac{9}{16} - \frac{1}{4}$ is the same as $\frac{36}{64} - \frac{16}{64} = \frac{20}{64}$.

If we reduce $\frac{20}{64}$ to lowest terms, we get a final answer of $\frac{5}{16}$ just as we got when we used the least common denominator 16.

When you add or subtract fractions with different denominators, you can use any common denominator. If you choose to use the least common denominator, your sum or difference will already be reduced to lowest terms. If you choose to use a common denominator, which is not the least common denominator, that is ok; but you should then reduce your sum or difference to lowest terms.

A SHORT QUIZ ON THE RULES

1. When do we add the denominators of fractions? ____________________

   ____

2. When do we add the numerators of fractions? ____________________

   ____

3. When do we subtract the denominators of fractions? ____________________

   ____

4. When do we subtract the numerators of fractions? ____________________

   ____

Drill for Skill (VI)

(Do NOT forget to find a common denominator)

1. $\frac{4}{9} - \frac{1}{3} =$ __________
2. $\frac{16}{32} - \frac{1}{4} =$ __________
3. $\frac{3}{8} - \frac{3}{16} =$ __________
4. $\frac{8}{12} - \frac{2}{6} =$ __________
5. $\frac{9}{16} - \frac{2}{8} =$ __________
6. $\frac{7}{3} - \frac{5}{12} =$ __________

Word Problems That Call for Addition of Fractions with Unlike Denominators

Now that you know how to add and subtract fractions with unlike denominators, let us try some word problems. Let's begin with addition. In looking at these word problems, remember **addition** means **to join, to accumulate**. Addition problems often give you key words like **altogether, combine, sum,** or **in all**. Once you have decided that the problem asks you to add, pull out the numbers. If the denominators are unlike, use your new skills to first find a common denominator. Then go ahead and add the fractions.

Example: Mrs. Haynes owned a small grocery store. One week she was ill and her children Mary and Dennis decided to help out. Mary spent $\frac{1}{3}$ day working in the store on Monday and Dennis spent $\frac{3}{4}$ day working there on Tuesday. How much time did the children spend working there in all? ________

Solution: The problem calls for **combining** the work times of the two persons and uses the key words **in all**. It is clear, therefore, that the problem calls for **addition**.

Pulling out the numbers, you have $\frac{1}{3} + \frac{3}{4}$. You can see the denominators are unlike. To add these fractions, you must first find a **common denominator**. What will both 3 and 4 go into exactly? Many numbers, but 12 is the least common denominator; we will use it.

Change $\frac{1}{3}$ into $\frac{?}{12}$

3 into 12 = 4

$\frac{1}{3} \times \frac{4}{4} = \frac{4}{12}$

Now change $\frac{3}{4}$ into $\frac{?}{12}$

4 into 12 = 3

$\frac{3}{4} \times \frac{3}{3} = \frac{9}{12}$

So we add $\frac{4}{12} + \frac{9}{12}$. As the denominators are now the same, we simply add the numerators and come up with $\frac{13}{12}$. Because $\frac{13}{12}$ is an improper fraction, we will change it into a mixed number. $\frac{13}{12} = 1\frac{1}{12}$. The problem asks how many days in all, so our answer is $1\frac{1}{12}$ days.

Name ______________________

Date ______________________

Reproducible

Word Problems for Practice (X)

1. During a power outage caused by a thunderstorm, Beverley lit a small candle to provide light. The candle burned for $\frac{1}{2}$ hour, then went out. She then lit a second candle which burned for another $\frac{3}{4}$ hour. For how long was there candlelight in the house?

   ____

2. A carpenter's helper had 4 bags of nails on the shelf. These bags of nails weighed as follows: $\frac{1}{4}$ lb, $\frac{1}{2}$ lb, $\frac{2}{3}$ lb, and $\frac{3}{4}$ lb. What was the combined weight of the bags of nails?

   ____

3. The manager of a toy factory was studying how much time workers spent in putting together children's toys. He got out his stop watch and timed one worker putting together a remote-controlled robot. The worker performed three tasks. One task took $\frac{2}{3}$ of a minute, the next took $\frac{3}{4}$ minute, and the third took $\frac{5}{8}$ minute. How much time did the worker spend on the three tasks in all?

   ____

4. Ernestine was playing piano for a New Year's Eve party. When midnight came, she played "Auld Lang Syne." As she read the notes, she saw that the first note lasted for $\frac{1}{4}$ beat, the second note was for $\frac{6}{16}$ beat, and that the third note was played for $\frac{1}{8}$ beat. What was the total time for the first three notes?

   ____

5. Three candidates ran for mayor of a big city. The first two candidates said they would cut taxes. The third candidate said he would raise them. The first candidate received $\frac{2}{5}$ of the vote. The second candidate received $\frac{7}{15}$ of the vote. What fraction of the vote did the two candidates who said they wanted to cut taxes receive?

   ____

6. Eloise took her ill-tempered dog to dog obedience school to try to improve his behavior. The dog attended one session for $\frac{3}{4}$ of an hour and a second session for $\frac{1}{6}$ of an hour. At that point, the dog began chewing up the instructor's rug and was suspended. How much time was the dog in school before becoming an obedience school dropout?

   ____

7. In Melissa's stamp collection, $1/4$ of the stamps were from European countries, $2/16$ were from Canada, $1/8$ were from Latin American countries, $1/16$ were from Asia and African countries, and the rest were from the United States. What fraction of the collection were from countries outside the United States?

   ____

8. The Chang family spent $1/2$ of their vacation time in California and $1/3$ of their time in the neighboring state of Arizona. They then flew back East to end their vacation time. What fraction of their vacation time did the Changs spend in the two western states?

   ____

9. The Greene family spent $1/3$ of their income for rent, $1/4$ for food, and $1/8$ for medical expenses. What part of their total income went for these expenses?

   ____

10. Carl's grandmother had surgery for her hip. She had a "hip replacement." As she was recovering, her doctor asked her to do some walking. In the morning, she walked $1/5$ mile. In the evening, she walked $1/4$ mile. How far did she travel altogether in these two walks?

    ____

Name ______________________________

Date ______________________________

Reproducible

Addition and Subtraction of Fractions with Unlike Denominators

Making Movies

Max and Winston were the two top script writers for Rip Roaring Motion Pictures. One afternoon they were seated in their Hollywood office and both looked worried. Their boss, Mr. Roaring, wanted a screenplay for a new science fiction film, and he wanted it in a hurry.

"I've got it. I've got it," Max said suddenly. "We'll cal it *The Blob That Ate Up the World.*"

"That ate up the what?" Winston replied.

Max spread out his hands. "You see," he said, "it's about this blob that comes from outer space. It lands outside of Los Angeles and starts eating everything in sight—trucks, timber, towns,—everything."

"Everything?"

"Sure. Imagine this big dark blob, oozing outward. It grows and grows. The first day it is $\frac{1}{4}$ kilometer long. The second day it grows by another $\frac{1}{2}$ kilometer. The third day by another $\frac{3}{4}$ kilometer. The fourth day. . ."

"Stop," Winston interrupted. "It's big enough already. How do we kill it?"

"Kill it? We don't. The blob wins. It eats up the whole planet."

"You're crazy," Winston replied. "Nobody will go to see a picture in which the Blob wins and all of us lose."

"They won't?"

"No. The Blob must go."

"O.K.," Max replied sadly. "We'll destroy it with an atomic ray gun or something."

With Winston's suggestion in mind, Max wrote the script. The picture was filmed with a cast of thousands and soon *The Blob That Almost Ate Up the World* was playing at movie houses across the nation. It was a great success, earning more than $40,000,000. Max and Winston were last seen at Pepy's Pizza Parlor planning their next film, *Return of the Blob.*

How big did the Blob get after 3 days of eating its way through southern California?

Name ______________________________

Date ______________________________

Reproducible

Word Problems That Call for Subtraction of Fractions with Unlike Denominators

To solve word problems that require us to subtract fractions with unlike denominators, we follow the same general approach we used with fractions having like denominators. First, we look at the logic of the problem. Does the problem ask for differences or what remains? If so, subtraction is in order. We pull out the numbers from the problem and do the arithmetic. This time, however, the arithmetic requires us to first find a common denominator and then to subtract the equivalent fractions having this common denominator.

Example: At Elmo's Hamburger Hut, the chef starts with hamburger patties that weigh $\frac{7}{8}$ of a pound. After the patties are cooked, they shrink to $\frac{1}{2}$ of a pound. How much weight is lost in the cooking? __________

Solution: This problem calls for finding the **difference** in the weights of the hamburgers; therefore we must subtract. Taking the numbers out, we have $\frac{7}{8} - \frac{1}{2}$. We can see that the fractions have unlike denominators, so before subtracting, we must find a common denominator. What do 2 and 8 both go into exactly? Many numbers: 16, 24, 48; but the least common denominator is 8, itself, so we shall use that.

$\frac{1}{2} = \frac{?}{8}$ 2 goes into 8, 4 times. $\frac{1}{2} \times \frac{4}{4} = \frac{4}{8}$

So $\frac{1}{2} = \frac{4}{8}$.

Now, we rewrite $\frac{7}{8} - \frac{1}{2}$ as $\frac{7}{8} - \frac{4}{8}$.

Subtracting these fractions gives us $\frac{3}{8}$. The answer is $\frac{3}{8}$ pound.

Word Problems for Practice (XI)

1. One motor had $\frac{7}{8}$ horsepower. A second motor had $\frac{1}{3}$ horsepower. How much less horsepower did the second motor have than the first? ________
2. José took a paper route as a part-time job. On the first day, he served his paper route in $\frac{3}{5}$ hour. The next day, he and his friend John served the same route in $\frac{3}{10}$ hour. How much faster were the two of them able to serve the route than José was able to when working alone? ________
3. A nurse had two needles in front of her to use for giving injections. One was $\frac{3}{4}$ inch long, the other $\frac{1}{2}$ inch long. How much longer was one needle that the other? ____________

Name ______________________________

Date ______________________________

Reproducible

Addition and Subtraction of Fractions with Unlike Denominators

4. At the first reunion of the 1990 graduating class of Lincoln High School, $\frac{3}{5}$ of the graduates showed up. At the second reunion of the 1990 class, only $\frac{1}{2}$ of the graduates appeared. By what fraction did attendance drop off?
____

5. Karen's parents were going to celebrate their 25th wedding anniversary. Karen went along with her father to the jewelry store where he wanted to buy a diamond for his wife. He looked at two diamonds. One weighed $\frac{1}{3}$ karat, the other weighed $\frac{1}{4}$ karat. What was the difference in weight between the two diamonds? ____________

6. The high school football coach was testing Bill and Jim to see how far they could run at full speed with all their equipment on. The coach yelled, "Start," and watched Bill and Jim run down the field. Then the coach looked at his stopwatch and yelled, "Stop." Between the time the coach yelled start and the time he yelled stop, Bill ran $\frac{7}{8}$ the length of the football field, while Jim ran $\frac{5}{6}$ the length of the football field.

   (a) Who ran faster? ____________

   (b) How much more of the field did the faster runner cover? ____________

7. In science class, the teacher compared two types of violets. The distance across the flower of the first violet, which had a white color, measured $\frac{2}{5}$ inch. The distance across the flower of the second violet, which had a purple color, measured $\frac{7}{12}$ inch. How much longer was the distance across the flower of the purple violet than the distance across the flower of the white violet? ____________

8. Two books were lying next to each other on a table. The first book was $\frac{13}{16}$" thick, the second book was $\frac{7}{8}$" thick. Which book was thicker and by how much? ____________

9. A scientist was exploring some woodland where he believed Native Americans had lived hundreds of years ago. He began digging a trench into the ground. One-third meter below the surface, he found a small arrowhead. Seven eights meter below the surface, he found some polished beads. How much deeper were the beads than the arrowhead? ____________

10. Stan was studying chemistry. In his first lab, the teacher told the students that it was very important to weigh things carefully and to record the results accurately in their lab books. Stan weighed out $\frac{7}{8}$ gram of sulphur and put it into his test tube. Then he slipped on a wet spot on the floor. The first thing he noticed was yellow powdery stuff on the floor. At that point, Stan really didn't know what to do. He just wanted to finish the lab. With that goal in mind, he decided to weigh the sulphur that remained in his test tube. If that sulphur weighed $\frac{1}{2}$ gram, how much more sulphur would Stan have to put into his test tube to reach the $\frac{7}{8}$ gram that he originally had? ____________

Addition and Subtraction of Mixed Numbers

Teacher Notes

Chapter 4 begins by reviewing the definition of a mixed number from Chapter 1. It then discusses the difference between adding mixed numbers whose fractions have like denominators and adding mixed numbers for which a least common denominator must be found (reviewing Chapter 3). Drills for Skill give students practice with the material. Finding the Missing Fractional part teaches students how to subtract a fraction from 1 to find what part would be needed to make the whole.

Answers

Drill for Skill VII:

1. $6\frac{1}{8}$, **2.** $8\frac{7}{8}$, **3.** $11\frac{3}{10}$, **4.** $8\frac{1}{4}$, **5.** $5\frac{1}{3}$, **6.** $9\frac{1}{6}$

Magic Carpet: $11\frac{2}{3}$, $11\frac{2}{3}$, $11\frac{2}{3}$, $11\frac{2}{3}$

Word Problems for Practice XII

1. $10\frac{13}{16}$ lbs., **2.** $7\frac{1}{3}$ km, **3.** $18\frac{1}{2}$ yds., **4.** $4\frac{7}{8}$ hrs., **5.** $5\frac{1}{6}$ ft., **6.** $112\frac{3}{4}$ lbs.

Word Problems for Practice XIII

1. $2\frac{5}{6}$ km., **2.** 16 yds., **3.** $8\frac{4}{5}$ km/sec, **4.** $1\frac{1}{2}$ yrs., **5.** $\frac{5}{8}$ min., **6.** $2\frac{5}{8}$ mi.

Word Problems for Practice XIV

1. $\frac{1}{5}$, **2.** $\frac{3}{5}$, **3.** $\frac{3}{4}$, **4.** $\frac{1}{3}$

Wild Pitch: $2\frac{2}{3}$ innings

Name ______________________________

Date ______________________________

Reproducible

Addition and Subtraction of Fractions with Unlike Denominators

You remember from Chapter 1 that a mixed number is a whole number and a fraction that are considered together as a single number. In other words, a mixed number is like a whole number and a fraction glued together. To complete our discussion of addition and subtraction of fractions, we will now explain how to add and subtract mixed numbers and to use these tools in solving word problems.

Let us begin with addition.

Handy Rule for Adding Mixed Numbers

1. First, change each mixed number into an improper fraction.
2. **If the denominators are the same**, add the fractions just as you added fractions whose denominators were alike.
3. **If the denominators are not the same:**
   (a) Find a common denominator.
   (b) Change each fraction into an equivalent fraction whose denominator is the common denominator.
   (c) Then add the equivalent fractions just like you added fractions whose denominators were alike.
4. Finally, simplify your answer by changing any improper fractions in the answer into either whole or mixed numbers.

Example where denominators are the same:

$2\frac{1}{2} + 3\frac{1}{2}$

Step 1. $\frac{5}{2} + \frac{7}{2}$

Step 2. $\frac{5}{2} + \frac{7}{2} = \frac{12}{2}$

The denominators were alike. We did not need to find a common denominator.

Step 3. $\frac{12}{2} = 6$

6 is the answer.

Example where denominators are not the same:

$2\frac{1}{3} + 3\frac{1}{10}$

Step 1. $\frac{7}{3} + \frac{31}{10}$

Step 2. Observe—the denominators are not the same.

a. A common denominator is 30.

b. $\frac{7}{3} + \frac{31}{10} = \frac{70}{30} + \frac{93}{30}$

c. $\frac{163}{30} = 5\frac{13}{30}$ Answer

Name ______________________

Date ______________________

Drill for Skill (VII)

Add the following mixed numbers.

1. $2\frac{7}{8} + 3\frac{2}{8} =$ ________
2. $2\frac{3}{4} + 6\frac{1}{8} =$ ________
3. $2\frac{1}{5} + 9\frac{1}{10} =$ ________
4. $3\frac{1}{2} + 4\frac{3}{4} =$ ________
5. $3\frac{3}{4} + 1\frac{7}{12} =$ ________
6. $2\frac{1}{2} + 6\frac{2}{3} =$ ________

Let's try a word problem in which we must add mixed numbers.

Example: Angela was building some book shelves for her new apartment. She made shelves using bricks and boards. The bottom shelf was $14\frac{1}{2}$ inches high, the middle shelf was 13 inches high, while the top shelf was $9\frac{3}{4}$ inches high. How high were the book shelves in all?

Solution: The problem asks for the combined height of the book shelves. It uses the key words **in all**. The problem clearly requires addition. The numbers are: $14\frac{1}{2}$, 13, and $9\frac{3}{4}$.

This problem is interesting! You can see that one number (13) is a **whole number**, while the other two numbers are mixed numbers. How do we add these? Keep reading!

A Handy Rule for Adding a Whole Numbers and Mixed Numbers

In a situation such as this, write the whole number over 1: $\frac{13}{1}$
you are then required to add:

$$14\frac{1}{2} + \frac{13}{1} + 9\frac{3}{4}$$

Step 1. Change the mixed numbers into improper fractions.

$$\frac{29}{2} + \frac{13}{1} + \frac{39}{4}$$

Step 2. The denominators are not the same, so

(a) Find a common denominator. A common denominator is 4.

(b) Then change each fraction into an equivalent fraction with a denominator of 4.

$$\frac{29}{2} = \frac{58}{4} \qquad \frac{13}{1} = \frac{52}{4} \qquad \frac{39}{4} = \frac{39}{4}$$

(c) Now add $\frac{58}{4} + \frac{52}{4} + \frac{39}{4} = \frac{149}{4}$.

Step 3. Change $\frac{149}{4}$ into a mixed number. This gives you $37\frac{1}{4}$.

The problem dealt with inches, so the **answer is $37\frac{1}{4}$ inches.**

Name ______________________________

Date ______________________________

A Handy Rule for Adding a Whole Number and a Fraction

It is easy to add a whole number and fraction. To do this, you can simply write the whole number followed by the fraction. Here are some examples.

$2 + \frac{1}{2} = 2\frac{1}{2}$ $\quad 3 + \frac{2}{5} = 3\frac{2}{5}$ $\quad 11 + \frac{7}{8} = 11\frac{7}{8}$

A MAGIC CARPET

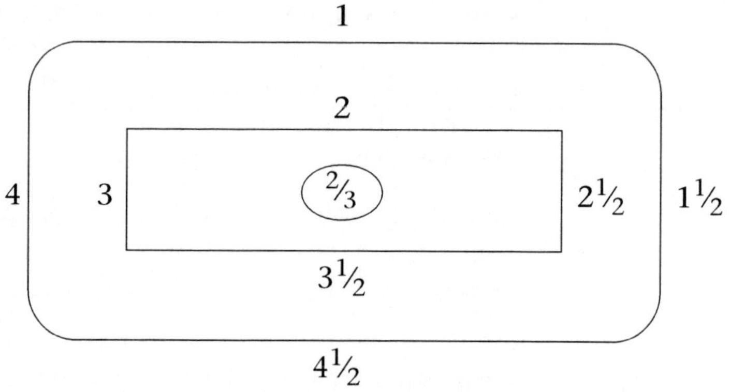

First, go across the carpet. Add all of the numbers as you go across (begin with 4, end with $1\frac{1}{2}$).

Now, let's go down the carpet. Add all of the numbers as you go down (begin with 1, end with $4\frac{1}{2}$).

Add the numbers as you move around the outside of the carpet. To that sum add the $\frac{2}{3}$ in the middle of the carpet.

Finally, add all the numbers as you go around the inside of the carpet. To that sum add the $\frac{2}{3}$ in the middle of the carpet.

Were you surprised that all these sums were the same? That's why this carpet is magic.

Word Problems for Practice (XII)

1. Two sisters took their clothes to the laundromat. The weight of one bundle of clothes was $4\frac{3}{4}$ lbs. The weight of the other bundle of clothes was $6\frac{1}{16}$ lbs. What was the total weight of the bundles? ____________

2. Three bicycle paths were laid out in the city park. They measured $1\frac{2}{3}$ kilometers, $2\frac{1}{5}$ kilometers, and $3\frac{7}{15}$ kilometers, respectively. What was the combined distance of the bicycle paths? ____________

3. A fullback carried the ball four times during a football game. During these carries, he gained 4 yards, 6 yards, 8 yards, and $\frac{1}{2}$ yard. How many yards did he gain altogether? ____________

4. Shirley went on a trip to visit her grandmother. From the time she left home until the time she reached her grandmother's house, she spent the following amounts of time: $\frac{1}{2}$ hour in a cab, 1 hour waiting at the airport, $2\frac{3}{4}$ hours in an airplane, and $\frac{5}{8}$ hour in a second cab. How much time did the trip take in all? ____________

5. Kaci was 5 feet tall. Over the summer, her height increased by $\frac{1}{6}$ foot. How tall was she then? ____________

6. Brittney weighed 112 pounds on her scale at home. If she weighed $\frac{3}{4}$ pound more on the scale at her doctor's office, how much did she weigh on that scale? ____________

Subtracting Mixed Numbers

A Handy Rule for Subtracting Mixed Numbers

To subtract mixed numbers, we **first change any mixed numbers into improper fractions**. Then follow the rules for subtracting fractions.

Example: $2\frac{2}{3} - 1\frac{1}{2}$ (Change the mixed numbers into improper fractions.)

$= \frac{8}{3} - \frac{3}{2}$ (A common denominator is 6!)

Change each fraction into an equivalent fraction whose denominator is 6. (Then subtract.) $= \frac{16}{6} - \frac{9}{6} = \frac{7}{6}$

Simplifying $\frac{7}{6}$ by writing it as an improper fraction, we get $1\frac{1}{6}$ as our answer.

Let's try a word problem.

Example: Little Ludwig was learning how to play the flute. His teacher was his cousin who was also named Ludwig and was called Big Ludwig by everyone. Little Ludwig had been playing the flute for $2\frac{1}{4}$ years. Big Ludwig had been playing the flute for $7\frac{1}{2}$ years. How much longer had Big Ludwig been playing the flute than little Ludwig? ____________

Solution: If you are puzzled by what to do, try restating the problem: What is the **difference** in the length of time Big Ludwig and Little Ludwig have played the flute? That should give you a clue to subtract.

Step 1. Here are the numbers: $7\frac{1}{2} - 2\frac{1}{4}$.

Step 2. Remember our arithmetic. First change these mixed numbers into improper fractions. $7\frac{1}{2} - 2\frac{1}{4} = \frac{15}{2} - \frac{9}{4}$

Step 3. Now look for a common denominator. That's easy, it's 4.

Step 4. Then change each fraction into an equivalent fraction whose denominator is 4. That gives $\frac{30}{4} - \frac{9}{4}$, or $\frac{21}{4}$.

Step 5. Change $\frac{21}{4}$ to a mixed number: $5\frac{1}{4}$

Step 6. $5\frac{1}{4}$ what? Years.

Word Problems for Practice (XIII)

1. Two Boy Scouts were hiking along a trail in the mountains. On the first day they walked $9\frac{1}{2}$ kilometers. On the second day they walked $12\frac{1}{3}$ kilometers. How much farther did they walk on the second day than the first?

   ____

2. During a football game there was a heavy wind. It was hard to punt (kick) the ball against the wind. Punts made with the wind averaged $50\frac{3}{4}$ yards. Punts made against the wind averaged $34\frac{3}{4}$ yards. What was the difference in yardage between punts made with the wind and against the wind?

   ____

3. A rocket ship must travel at a speed of $11\frac{2}{10}$ kilometers per second to leave the earth and go into space. To leave the moon, the rocket ship must travel at a speed of $2\frac{4}{10}$ kilometers per second. How much faster must a rocket ship travel to leave the earth than to leave the moon? ____________

4. A spacecraft was sent into orbit around the earth to gather information about the earth's atmosphere. The spacecraft was designed to send information back to government laboratories for 3 years. After $1\frac{1}{2}$ years had elapsed, how much time remained for the spacecraft's mission? __________
5. Ron purchased a desktop publishing computer program to use in making up a newsletter. First he tried the program on his own computer, and then he tried the program on his friend Marcia's computer. His computer ran the program in $1\frac{3}{4}$ minutes. Marcia's computer ran the program in $1\frac{1}{8}$ minutes. What was the difference in the times it took these computers to run this program? __________
6. The *Mary Ellen* was a sailboat that was equipped to look for sunken treasure. A very old weather-beaten map indicated that a ship loaded with Spanish gold had sunk $2\frac{1}{4}$ miles east of a point on the shoreline called Pirates' Cove. The crew of the *Mary Ellen* used modern sonar equipment to locate the sunken ship. They found that the ship was $4\frac{7}{8}$ miles east of Pirates' Cove. How much farther away from Pirates' Cove was the sunken ship than the old map indicated? __________

Some Final Words on Subtraction

In subtraction problems which contain

BOTH A WHOLE NUMBER AND A MIXED NUMBER
OR
BOTH A WHOLE NUMBER AND A FRACTION:

(a) First write the whole number over 1.

(b) Then use the rules you have already learned for subtraction.

Example A:	**Hints**	**Example B:**
$2 - 1\frac{1}{3}$		$2 - \frac{7}{8}$
$= \frac{2}{1} - 1\frac{1}{3}$	(Write the whole number over 1.)	$= \frac{2}{1} - \frac{7}{8}$
$= \frac{2}{1} - \frac{4}{3}$	(Change the mixed number into an improper fraction.)	$= \frac{16}{8} - \frac{7}{8}$
$= \frac{6}{3} - \frac{4}{3}$	(3 is a common denominator.)	$= \frac{9}{8}$
$= \frac{2}{3}$ Answer		$= 1\frac{1}{8}$ Answer

Name ______________________________

Date ______________________________

Finding the Missing Fractional Part

Sometimes word problems **give us a fractional part of something**, and they **ask us to find the fractional part of the thing that is left**. To solve such a problem, **subtract the given fractional part from the number 1**.

Example: A man was building a doll house for his daughter. After he finished $\frac{3}{5}$ of the house, how much of the house remained to be built?

Solution: You are dealing with 1 whole house. You know that $\frac{3}{5}$ of the house has been completed. You are asked, "What fractional part of the house is left to be built?"

The answer is found by subtraction.

$$1 - \frac{3}{5} = \frac{1}{1} - \frac{3}{5} = \frac{5}{5} - \frac{3}{5} = \frac{2}{5}$$

Two fifths of the house remained to be built.

Another Example: As we learned in Chapter 1 (Introduction to Fractions), we sometimes deal with fractional parts of a collection of things. An example might be the fractional part of the total number of games that a team wins during a season or the fractional part of the total number of games that a team loses during a season. You could have a problem like this.

During the season, the Jackson College Basketball Team won $\frac{5}{8}$ of their games. What fractional part of their games did they lose?

Solution: The problem says that $\frac{5}{8}$ of their games were won. You are asked for the fractional part of their games lost. In other words, you are asked to find the missing fractional part of the total games played.

Subtract $1 - \frac{5}{8}$

$$= \frac{1}{1} - \frac{5}{8}$$

$$= \frac{8}{8} - \frac{5}{8} = \frac{3}{8}$$

Answer: They lost $\frac{3}{8}$ of their games.

Word Problems for Practice (XIV)

Do these problems in the same way. Remember to subtract the fractional part you are given from 1.

1. During the summer, Chris and Harriet played tennis almost every day. Chris won $4/5$ of the matches. What fraction of the matches did Harriet win?

   ____

2. Four tenths of the players on the Columbus High School football team were seniors. What fraction of the players were not seniors? __________
3. Alice's father bought a new house. One fourth of the heat in the house came from solar panels on the roof. The remaining heat came from natural gas. What part of the heat came from natural gas? __________
4. If you mix red paint with yellow paint, you will get orange paint. If you mix more red and less yellow, you'll get a darker orange color. If a bucket is $2/3$ full of red paint, what fraction of this bucket is left for yellow paint?

   ____

   What color do you think you would get by mixing red and blue? If you said "violet," your answer is correct.

Wild Pitch

Bill "Bean-ball" Baxter wanted to be a baseball pitcher. The scouting reports on Baxter said he had "good stuff"—a fast ball that zoomed, a wide-sweeping curve ball, and a knuckle ball that danced in front of the batter's eyes. Baxter's problem was control. He didn't have any. When Baxter threw the ball, no one was quite sure where the ball was going to end up and that included Baxter.

Baxter joined a minor league baseball team and went out to the mound to pitch his first game. After 4 innings, the manager had to remove Baxter from the game. It seemed that Baxter had nicked 3 batters in a row with his fast ball (one on the arm, one on the shoulder, and one on the seat of his baseball uniform—which is a difficult trick to accomplish when you are facing someone). The opposing team was about ready to go after Baxter with their bats when the manager, fearing that a riot would break out, took Baxter out of the game.

The next time Baxter pitched, he was still a bit wild, walking the first 10 men he faced and hitting the 11th. After $1\frac{1}{3}$ innings, his manager had seen enough and took him out of the game.

How many more innings did Baxter pitch in his first game than in his second game? __________

Multiplying with Fractions

Teacher Notes

X

This chapter begins by emphasizing the idea that when we multiply by a proper fraction, the product is smaller than the numbers the student starts with, noting that finding *a fractional part of something* is often a signal to multiply. The following lessons also discuss how to find other phrases in word problems that are often signals to multiply, such as *reduced by a fractional part, a fractional part as far as,* and *a fractional part as much as.*

Answers

Drill for Skill VIII:
1. $\frac{7}{12}$, **2.** $\frac{4}{45}$, **3.** $\frac{9}{100}$, **4.** $\frac{1}{3}$

Word Problems for Practice XV
1. $\frac{1}{6}$ yr., **2.** $\frac{1}{6}$ *l*, **3.** $\frac{1}{8}$ of the game, **4.** $\frac{1}{4}$ hr., **5.** $\$\frac{1}{2}$ million, **6.** $\frac{1}{8}$ hr., **Hot Air:** $\frac{3}{8}$ hr.

Drill for Skill IX
1. 8, **2.** $109\frac{3}{8}$, **3.** 900, **4.** $17\frac{7}{16}$, **5.** 640

Word Problems for Practice XVI
1. 60 mi., 120 mi., **2.** \$1,550, **3.** 40 hrs., **4.** \$100 **5.** 50 bicycles, **6.** \$13, **7.** \$20 **8. a.** \$120,000, **8. b.** \$60,000, **8. c.** \$60,000, **9.** \$13, **10.** 8 scientists, **Trial by Jury:** \$20,000

Some Problems to Try
1. \$3, **2.** 120 m.

Word Problems for Practice XVII
1. \$43.50, **2.** \$260, **3.** \$15, **4.** 105 hrs., **5.** \$23, **6.** $192\frac{1}{2}$ mi., **7.** $17\frac{1}{2}$ hrs., **8.** 100 hrs., **Shooting Stars:** 6 meteors **b.** 25 meteors, **c.** 6 meteors.

Name ______________________________

Date ______________________________

Multiplying with Fractions

Do you remember multiplying whole numbers like 9×6, or 1523×79? The answer got big quickly. Sometimes the answers got so large you couldn't even get them on a pocket calculator. Well, here's a surprise for you. When you multiply any number except 0 by a fraction that is less than 1, the result is SMALLER than the number with which you started.

Smaller? "How can it be," you might ask, "that when you multiply something by a fraction that is less than one, the something gets smaller?" We admit it sounds strange at first, but you will find that's the way it is. Let us begin by looking at what happens when you multiply a fraction by a fraction.

Multiplying a Fraction by a Fraction

Let's start with an example.

What is $\frac{1}{2}$ of one dollar? 
The answer: half a dollar.
Now what is $\frac{1}{2}$ **of half** a dollar? One quarter.
So, $\frac{1}{2}$ of $\frac{1}{2} = \frac{1}{4}$.

Name ______________________________

Date ______________________________

Here's another example.

Imagine a hot pizza, loaded with peppers, anchovies, mushrooms, and sausages.

You cut off $\frac{1}{4}$ of it.

Your slice ($\frac{1}{4}$)

Now, suppose a friend with hungry eyes comes along and you give her $\frac{1}{2}$ of your slice.

So $\frac{1}{2}$ **of** $\frac{1}{4}$ looks like this: 

Put her slice back into the original pizza and you can see it's $\frac{1}{8}$ of the original pizza.

So $\frac{1}{2}$ **of** $\frac{1}{4} = \frac{1}{8}$ 

From the above example, we can see that when we take $\frac{1}{2}$ **of** something, the result is smaller than the thing with which we started.

Let's look at some more pictures. This time, start with $\frac{1}{2}$ of a pizza. And take $\frac{2}{3}$ of that. What do we get?

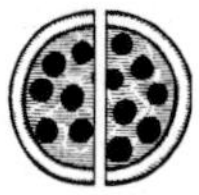

$\frac{2}{3}$ of $\frac{1}{2}$ = 

You can find out by putting your slice back into the original pizza.

If you mark up the pizza the way we have here, you can see that your slice is $\frac{2}{6}$ of the pizza.

So $\frac{2}{3}$ **of** $\frac{1}{2} = \frac{2}{6}$, which reduces to $\frac{1}{3}$.

When we take a fractional part of something, the answer is always less than the thing with which we started. In math, finding a fractional part **of** something means to multiply. So, in the above examples, we have

$\frac{1}{2}$ **of** $\frac{1}{2} = \frac{1}{2} \times \frac{1}{2} = \frac{1}{4}$

$\frac{1}{2}$ **of** $\frac{1}{4} = \frac{1}{2} \times \frac{1}{4} = \frac{1}{8}$

$\frac{2}{3}$ **of** $\frac{1}{2} = \frac{2}{3} \times \frac{1}{2} = \frac{2}{6}$ (which reduces to $\frac{1}{3}$)

A Handy Rule for Multiplying a Fraction by a Fraction

1. Multiply the numerators (tops) together to get the numerator of your answer.
2. Multiply the denominators (bottoms) together to get the denominator of your answer.

Example: $\frac{1}{2} \times \frac{1}{2} = \frac{1 \times 1}{2 \times 2} = \frac{1}{4}$

Drill for Skill (VIII)

1. $\frac{7}{8}$ of $\frac{2}{3}$ = ______________
2. $\frac{4}{9}$ of $\frac{1}{5}$ = ______________
3. $\frac{1}{10}$ of $\frac{9}{10}$ = ______________
4. $\frac{2}{3} \times \frac{3}{6}$ = ______________

Name ______________________

Date ______________________

Key Words for Multiplying by a Fraction

In solving word problems that ask us to multiply by a fraction, the most important thing to remember is one key word, and that key word is OF.

A Handy Rule for Remembering When to Multiply

When you see the word **of** in a problem which asks you **to find a fractional part of something**, remember to **multiply**.

Example: A runner was practicing on a half-mile track. He started out at full speed, but after running $\frac{3}{4}$ **of** the distance, he stopped, because of a pulled hamstring muscle. How far did he run before stopping?

Solution: You are asked **to find a fractional part of something**. Before stopping, the runner ran $\frac{3}{4}$ of the distance or $\frac{3}{4}$ of $\frac{1}{2}$ mile. Therefore, the answer is found by multiplying $\frac{3}{4} \times \frac{1}{2} = \frac{3}{8}$. We are talking about miles, so the answer is $\frac{3}{8}$ mile.

WATCH OUT: Sometimes word problems ask you to **find a fractional part of something** but the problems may not use the key word **of** in them. When this happens, you still **multiply**. Here is an example of such a problem.

Example: An ice cream freezer holds $\frac{7}{8}$ gallon. When the freezer is $\frac{1}{2}$ full, how much ice cream is in it?

Solution: You are asked to find how much the ice cream freezer holds when $\frac{1}{2}$ of it is full. In other words, you are asked to find a fractional part of something or $\frac{1}{2}$ of what the freezer holds when full or $\frac{1}{2}$ of $\frac{7}{8}$ gallon

OR $\frac{1}{2} \times \frac{7}{8}$ gallon $= \frac{7}{16}$ gallon.

Are there other key words or phrases that suggest multiplication? At times, you will see phrases such as

1. Something **has been reduced by a fraction** (The price of a bikini **has been reduced by $\frac{1}{2}$.**).
2. A sweater is $\frac{1}{3}$ **off**.
3. Something **has been increased by a fraction** (The price of meat is up by $\frac{1}{4}$.).

Name ______________________________

Date ______________________________

Reproducible

Multiplying with Fractions

When you see phrases like this, multiply to find

1. How much the item has been reduced.
2. How much the price has been slashed.
3. How much the item has been increased.

Example:	An old movie theater that had run into hard times was up for sale. The owners had asked for $\frac{1}{4}$ million dollars, but nobody was interested in buying the theater. The owners reduced the price by $\frac{1}{2}$. By how much was the price reduced?
Solution:	"Reduced By a Fraction" is a clue to multiply. Multiply the old price ($\frac{1}{4}$ million dollars) by $\frac{1}{2}$ (the fraction by which the price had been reduced).
	$\frac{1}{4} \times \frac{1}{2} = \frac{1}{8}$. The answer is $\frac{1}{8}$ million dollars.

Here is one more set of clues for which you can look. When you see phrases such as $\frac{1}{4}$ **as many**, $\frac{2}{5}$ **as much**, or $\frac{1}{8}$ **as far**, you will also probably have to multiply.

Example:	Two boys were being tested for speed on their bicycles. When a starting signal was given, they began riding as fast as they could, until a second signal was given telling them to stop. During this time, the first boy rode $\frac{5}{6}$ kilometer. The second boy rode only $\frac{2}{3}$ as far as the first boy. How far did the second boy ride?
Solution:	The key phrase AS FAR AS is your clue to multiply. Multiply the distance the first boy rode ($\frac{5}{6}$ kilometer) by the fractional part the second boy rode of this distance ($\frac{2}{3}$), and this will give you the second boy's distance.
	$\frac{5}{6} \times \frac{2}{3} = \frac{10}{18} = \frac{5}{9}$. The answer is $\frac{5}{9}$ kilometer.

Word Problems for Practice (XV)

1. Winter is $\frac{1}{4}$ of the year. What fraction of the year is $\frac{2}{3}$ of the winter?

   ____

2. After coming home from school, Mary was very thirsty. She found $\frac{1}{2}$ liter of cola in the refrigerator. Mary drank $\frac{1}{3}$ of what there was in the bottle. How much cola did she drink? ______________

3. Halfway through the first quarter of play of the football game, Carver High was in a scoreless tie with Kingston High. What fraction of the game had been completed?

   ____

4. The guitar player of a rock group was late for a performance at a school dance. The musicians were supposed to play for $\frac{3}{4}$ of an hour before taking a break. After $\frac{1}{3}$ of the performance was over, the guitar player finally showed up. How much of the $\frac{3}{4}$ hour performance had he missed?

   ____

5. Mr. Morgan invested $\frac{2}{3}$ million dollars in mining stocks. Shortly afterward, a large amount of silver was discovered in one of the company's mines. The stock increased in value by $\frac{3}{4}$. By how much money did the value of the stock increase?

   ____

6. Elaine's mother said Elaine wasn't relaxed enough. So Elaine decided to try some relaxation exercises she had read about in a book. Every morning she sat on the floor with her legs crossed for $\frac{1}{2}$ hour. For $\frac{1}{4}$ of this time, she closed her eyes and tried to think of lying on the beach in the hot sun. How much time did she spend thinking of this pleasant scene?

   ____

Hot Air

A politician wrote a speech on water pollution. The speech lasted $\frac{3}{4}$ hour. The politician, who liked the sound of his own voice, thought the speech seemed kind of short. He told his aide he was going to make it longer. His aide replied that the speech was too long already and to make it longer would change water pollution into air pollution. The politician muttered something unprintable and went ahead and lengthened the speech anyway. If he increased the $\frac{3}{4}$ hour speech by $\frac{1}{2}$ of this time, how much time would he have added to his speech?

____

Name ______________________________

Date ______________________________

Multiplying a Whole Number by a Fraction

Let's see if you can discover a rule. Take the numbers 4 (a whole number) and $\frac{1}{4}$ (a fraction). If we multiplied these numbers, it would be just the same as asking "What is 4 times a quarter—or how much are four quarters?" Now we know the answer to that is one dollar.

So $4 \times \frac{1}{4} = 1$. Now, how could we work that out?

A Handy Rule for Multiplying a Whole Number by a Fraction

1. Write the whole number over 1.
2. Then use the rule you learned for multiplying fractions. ($\frac{\text{Top} \times \text{Top}}{\text{Bottom} \times \text{Bottom}}$)

Example: $4 \times \frac{1}{4} = \frac{4}{1} \times \frac{1}{4} = \frac{4}{4}$. But, $\frac{4}{4} = 1$.

Let's try another problem, $12 \times \frac{2}{8}$.

Example: $12 \times \frac{2}{8} = \frac{12}{1} \times \frac{2}{8} = \frac{24}{8}$. ($\frac{\text{Top} \times \text{Top}}{\text{Bottom} \times \text{Bottom}}$)

$\frac{24}{8} = 3$ (Change $\frac{24}{8}$ into a whole number.)

Drill for Skill (IX)

1. $\frac{1}{2} \times 16 =$ ______________
2. $125 \times \frac{7}{8} =$ ______________
3. $1200 \times \frac{3}{4} =$ ______________
4. $\frac{9}{16} \times 31 =$ ______________
5. $960 \times \frac{2}{3} =$ ______________

Word Problems for Practice (XVI)

Look for the Key Words.

1. Suppose you were driving your car on a trip of 180 miles. You look at the map and you can see that you have gone $\frac{1}{3}$ of the distance. How many miles have you already traveled? ______________

Well, I've gone $\frac{1}{3}$ of 180 miles. I know that the word "of" is a signal to multiply, when I am looking for a fractional part of something. $\frac{1}{3} \times 180$ is $\frac{180}{3}$. Simplify, and that's 60. So, I've gone 60 miles.

Suppose you had gone $\frac{2}{3}$ of the distance. How many miles would you have traveled? ______________

2. George was starting his first job. He was being paid $15,500 a year. He wanted to put $\frac{1}{10}$ of his salary into a savings account. If he were able to do this for a year, how much would he save? ______________

3. Teresa was studying for an Associate of Arts degree at her community college. To get her degree, she needed to complete 60 hours of study. She had now finished $\frac{2}{3}$ of the course work. How many hours had she completed? ______________

4. If a lawyer charged $125 an hour for his services, how much money would he make in $\frac{4}{5}$ of an hour? ______________

5. A bicycle store usually sold 150 bicycles each month. During one month when there was a gasoline shortage, sales increased by $\frac{1}{3}$. How many more bicycles were sold during that month than were usually sold? ______________

6. Mrs. Johnson ordered a small bookcase for $130. She left $\frac{1}{10}$ of this sum as a deposit and agreed to pay the rest upon delivery. How many dollars did she leave on deposit? ______________

7. Before Christmas, a sweater sold for $60. After Christmas it was marked down by $\frac{1}{3}$ of its original price. By how many dollars had the price been reduced?

   ____

8. "Pop" Wheeler was athletic director of a small college. He had a budget of $240,000. One half of the budget was to be devoted to football, one quarter to basketball, and the remaining $\frac{1}{4}$ of the budget to all the rest of the sports (track, tennis, etc.).

   (a) How much money was to be used for football? ______________

   (b) How much for basketball? ______________

   (c) How much for the rest of the sports? ______________

9. A store at the mall advertised a special on jeans. If you purchased one pair of jeans for $26, you could buy a second pair for only $\frac{1}{2}$ of this price. How much would the second pair of jeans cost if you purchased the first pair?

   ____

10. Scientists were planning a trip to the Amazon Rain Forest in South America to collect plants that might be useful sources of new medicines. Twenty-four people would be involved with the work. One third of the people would be scientists. The rest of the people would be suppport staff (for example, guides, drivers, cooks, and student volunteers). How many scientists would be included in this project?

Name ______________________________

Date ______________________________

× Reproducible

Multiplying with Fractions

Trial by Jury

Mr. Barnes was riding along in his car and suddenly had to make a quick stop to avoid hitting a dog that was standing in the street. A car driven by Ms. Potter came up behind Mr. Barnes' car and slammed right smack into him. Mr. Barnes was treated for bruises, backache, and emotional problems following the accident. Mr. Barnes sued Ms. Potter. When the case came to trial, the well-known lawyer Mr. Grant made such a moving speech to the jury that Mr. Barnes was awarded 3 million dollars for his injuries. The judge, in his wisdom, said the award was much too high, and cut this figure to \$60,000. Mr. Grant asked for his fee, which was $\frac{1}{3}$ of this award. How much did he receive? __________

OTHER SIGNALS TO MULTIPLY:

Besides the key words and phrases which we have already discussed, another signal that tells us to multiply is a problem which calls for ADDING THE SAME THING SEVERAL TIMES.

Example If one hamburger patty uses $\frac{1}{4}$ pound of meat, how many pounds of meat are needed for 6 patties?

Solution Well, that would be

$$\frac{1}{4} + \frac{1}{4} + \frac{1}{4} + \frac{1}{4} + \frac{1}{4} + \frac{1}{4}$$

or $\frac{1}{4}$ six times, which is $6 \times \frac{1}{4} = \frac{6}{1} \times \frac{1}{4} = \frac{6}{4} = \frac{3}{2}$.

So, the answer is $\frac{3}{2}$ pounds or $1\frac{1}{2}$ pounds.

Some Problems to Try

1. Mrs. Guevara wanted to buy a dozen oranges in the supermarket. If the oranges were selling at a quarter each, how much would she have to pay for a dozen? ______________

2. When George walks, his steps are about $\frac{1}{2}$ meter long. If George walked 240 steps, about how many meters would he cover? ______________

Multiplying with Mixed Numbers

We learned that when we multiply any number except 0 by a fraction less than 1, our answer is smaller than the number with which we started.

What happens when you multiply a number by 1? Think about it.

$5 \times 1 = 5$ $\qquad$ $\frac{3}{4} \times 1 = \frac{3}{4}$

You get exactly the **same** number as the number with which you started.

The first thing to realize about multiplying by **mixed numbers** is that a mixed number always has a value **larger than 1**. (Think about it: $1\frac{1}{2}$, $1\frac{3}{8}$, $2\frac{5}{8}$ are all larger than 1.) Therefore when you multiply any number except 0 by a mixed number, the result will always be **bigger** than the number with which you started.

KEEP THIS IN MIND:

1. When you multiply any number except 0 by a fraction that is less than 1, the result is smaller than the number with which you started.
2. When you multiply any number by 1, the result is the same as the number with which you started.
3. When you multiply any number except 0 by a mixed number, the result is larger than the number with which you started.

A Handy Rule for Multiplying Mixed Numbers

In a multiplication problem which has mixed numbers in it, **first change all mixed numbers into improper fractions** and then multiply according to the rule for multiplying fractions:

$2\frac{1}{2} \times 3 = \frac{5}{2} \times \frac{3}{1} = \frac{15}{2} = 7\frac{1}{2}$ $\qquad$ $2\frac{1}{2} \times 3\frac{1}{2} = \frac{5}{2} \times \frac{7}{2} = \frac{35}{4} = 8\frac{3}{4}$

Word Problems for Practice (XVII)

1. Lexie bought 3 tee shirts which had the name of her sister's university printed on them in big gold letters. If the tee shirts cost $14\frac{1}{2}$ dollars each, what was the total cost of the 3 tee shirts?

   ____

2. The music book for the school band cost $6\frac{1}{2}$ dollars. There were 40 students in the band. If all the students bought books, what would be the total cost?

   ____

Name ______________________

Date ______________________

Reproducible

3. Marty was making $7\frac{1}{2}$ dollars an hour doing construction work. He joined Sibley Builders as a foreman at twice that pay. How much money was he now making per hour?

   ____

4. Students from Lincoln High School volunteered to put a new coat of paint on the walls of the Senior Citizens' Center. Thirty students participated. They each spent $3\frac{1}{2}$ hours painting the Center. How many work hours did these students paint?

   ____

5. During the summer, Rachel got a job helping out in Dr. Feldon's Animal Hospital, mainly holding unruly cats and dogs who were being given shots. Rachel worked 4 hours each day and was paid $5\frac{3}{4}$ dollars an hour. How much money did she make a day?

   ____

6. Bill's family was vacationing in California. They were driving from Los Angeles to San Francisco at a speed averaging 55 miles per hour. How far did they travel in $3\frac{1}{2}$ hours?

   ____

7. Ms. Jackson had to make a long drive through heavy traffic to get back and forth to her office. Each day, she spent $3\frac{1}{2}$ hours in her car to make these trips. During her 5-day work-week, how many hours did she spend during these drives?

   ____

8. Councilor Sturdlee didn't think the students were learning enough. He proposed that the school-day should be lengthened by $1\frac{1}{4}$ hours. Debra, who was very good in math, figured that in a 20-day period, (about a month of school days), Sturdlee's proposal would mean 25 more hours of school. John asked Debra how many more hours Sturdlee's proposal would add to 80 school days. What is the answer to John's question?

   ____

   The students took a poll about the Councilor's proposal. There was one vote for it, and 242 votes were cast against it.

Shooting Stars

It was the 11th of August. The time was after midnight. Jessica was sound asleep. The sound of a voice coming from below her window awakened her. It was Rachel from down the street. "Get up!" Rachel called, "if you want to watch the meteors." Jessica yawned, arose then woke her brother Rick. They quickly got dressed, joined Rachel, and the three lay down on blankets in a dark area behind the house. Rachel was a top science student and knew that a meteor shower came every year at this time—almost like clockwork.

The night was a beautifully clear night. The sky sparkled with stars. The children gasped when they saw the meteors flash across the sky like shooting stars. Some were colored; some, white like the stars. Some left trails. Rachel saw the most meteors. She counted 30. Rick saw the fewest. (He was half asleep.) He counted only $\frac{1}{5}$ as many as Rachel. Jessica was right behind Rachel. She counted $\frac{5}{6}$ as many as Rachel.

(a) How many meteors did Rick count? ______________

(b) How many did Jessica count? ______________

Rachel said that about $\frac{1}{5}$ of the meteors she saw were colored.

(c) About how many of the meteors that Rachel saw were colored? ______________

Dividing with Fractions

Teacher Notes

Chapter 6 begins with a review of the terms used in division: *dividend, divisor,* and *quotient.* It then introduces the concept of inverting the divisor and multiplying in order to divide a fraction by another fraction. The next lesson deals with dividing a fraction by a whole number (except 0): writing the number over the numeral one and proceeding as above. This is followed by the procedure for dividing with mixed numbers. As with the other operations with fractions, a section is devoted to finding the key words in word problems that are signals to divide, showing how to set up the equation: *how many are contained?, per, each person's share,* and so on. Word problems for practice with division are followed by a lesson on finding the whole when a part is known. The chapter closes with a review test of all operations with fractions.

Answers

Drill for Skill X:
1. 3, **2.** $3\frac{1}{3}$, **3.** $1\frac{2}{5}$, **4.** 24

Drill for Skill XI
1. $\frac{1}{8}$, **2.** $13\frac{1}{2}$, **3.** $\frac{7}{24}$, **4.** 40, **5.** $\frac{1}{16}$

Drill for Skill XII
1. $\frac{3}{8}$, **2.** 10, **3.** $\frac{20}{33}$, **4.** $\frac{3}{28}$, **5.** $\frac{5}{12}$, **6.** $2\frac{2}{5}$

Some Problems to Try
1. $\frac{11}{16}$ km., **2.** 8 cans, **3.** $\$10\frac{1}{4}$

Word Problems for Practice XVIII
1. $\frac{1}{4}$ box, **2.** $\frac{1}{8}$ hr., **3.** 80 quarters, **4.** $\frac{1}{8}$ lb., **5.** 9 times, **6.** $5\frac{1}{3}$ pp., **7.** $\frac{7}{12}$ m., **8.** 40 files

A Problem to Try
a. $1\frac{1}{2}$ hr., **b.** $\frac{1}{3}$, **c.** $1\frac{1}{2}$ hrs.

Word Problems for Practice XIX
1. $1\frac{1}{3}$ c., **2.** $1\frac{7}{20}$ hrs., **3.** \$2, **4.** $\frac{15}{16}$ *l.*, **5.** $3\frac{3}{4}$ qts., **6.** 27 stu., **7.** 12 hrs., **8.** 250,000 votes.

Word Problem Review Test
1. $18\frac{1}{6}$ gal., **2.** $14\frac{1}{2}$ tons, **3.** 160 students, **4.** 3 hrs., **5.** $\$2\frac{1}{4}$, **6.** \$15, **7.** $\frac{1}{10}$, **8.** $8\frac{1}{2}$ tons, **9.** $\frac{1}{2}$ hr, **10.** $1\frac{1}{16}$ in., **11.** $\frac{11}{12}$, **12.** \$45, **13.** $1\frac{2}{3}$ m., **14.** $\frac{13}{16}$ in., **15.** $\frac{1}{2000}$ sec., **16.** 30 cards, **17.** $7\frac{1}{2}$ hrs., **18.** $\frac{1}{6}$ hr.

Name ______________________________ Reproducible

Date ______________________________

Dividing with Fractions

In some ways, dividing with fractions is like dividing with whole numbers. For one thing the words are the same.

The number we divide is called the **dividend.**

The number we divide by is called the **divisor.**

The answer is called the **quotient.**

In this problem, $6 \div 2 = 3$,

6 is the **dividend.**
2 is the **divisor.**
3 is the **quotient.**

In this problem, $6 \div \frac{1}{2} =$ __________

6 is the **dividend.**
$\frac{1}{2}$ is the **divisor**, and the answer, which is what we will learn to find, is the **quotient.**

$6 \div 2$ MEANS **how many 2's are there in 6**? (Of course, the answer is 3)

$6 \div \frac{1}{2}$ MEANS **how many $\frac{1}{2}$'s are there in 6**? To get the answer to this question, look at the 6 ice-cream cones below. They have each been cut into halves. How many halves are there in the 6 cones?

The answer is 12. Do you see something interesting?

$6 \div \frac{1}{2}$ is the same as $6 \times \frac{2}{1} = \frac{6}{1} \times \frac{2}{1} = \frac{12}{1}$ or 12.

What is $3 \div \frac{3}{4}$?

Well, this means how many three-fourths are in 3?

Imagine you went to the bank with 3 one-dollar bills in your pocket. You went to the teller and you gave her one of the one-dollar bills. If you asked for change in quarters, she would give you 4 quarters.

Now suppose you gave her your second one-dollar bill and asked for change in quarters. She would give you 4 more quarters.

Finally, suppose you gave her your third one-dollar bill and asked for change in quarters. She would give you 4 more quarters.

Altogether, the teller has given 12 quarters (4 + 4 + 4) for your 3 dollars.

Now think of the question as how many groups of 3 quarters (three fourths) are there in these 12 quarters?

If you take the **twelve** quarters the teller has given you and make groups of quarters by putting **three** quarters in each group, you can find out.

HERE IS THE CHANGE THE TELLER HAS GIVEN YOU FOR YOUR 3 ONE-DOLLAR BILLS:

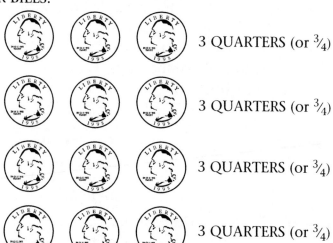

3 QUARTERS (or $\frac{3}{4}$)

3 QUARTERS (or $\frac{3}{4}$)

3 QUARTERS (or $\frac{3}{4}$)

3 QUARTERS (or $\frac{3}{4}$)

You can see there are **4** groups.

The money that you originally had in your pocket, the **3** one-dollar bills, has been changed into groups of quarters with three quarters ($\frac{3}{4}$) in each group. There are **4** of these groups.

Therefore there are **4** three-fourths in 3, OR $3 \div \frac{3}{4} = 4$.

Again, we see the interesting thing happening!

$3 \div \frac{3}{4} = 3 \times \frac{4}{3} = \frac{3}{1} \times \frac{4}{3} = \frac{12}{3} = 4$

What is this interesting thing that happens when we divide by fractions?

Look at the examples we have done, and you will see that when we divided a number by a fraction, the answer could be found by:

1. Turning the number we were dividing by upside down:

   $\frac{1}{2}$ upside down is $\frac{2}{1}$

   $\frac{1}{4}$ upside down is $\frac{4}{1}$

   $\frac{3}{4}$ upside down is $\frac{4}{3}$

   and then . . .

2. multiplying.

A Handy Rule for Dividing by a Fraction

To divide by a fraction, simply turn the fraction you are dividing by upside down and then multiply.

Example:	$6 \div \frac{2}{3} = 6 \times \frac{3}{2} = \frac{18}{2} = 9$
Example:	$\frac{1}{2} \div \frac{1}{4} = \frac{1}{2} \times \frac{4}{1} = \frac{4}{2} = 2$

Does this rule hold for dividing by **any** fraction? Yes, indeed, as long as the numerator of the fraction you are dividing by is not 0.

Drill for Skill (X)

See if you can find these **quotients**.

1. $\frac{1}{2} \div \frac{1}{6} =$ ______________
2. $\frac{2}{3} \div \frac{1}{5} =$ ______________
3. $\frac{7}{8} \div \frac{5}{8} =$ ______________
4. $12 \div \frac{1}{2} =$ ______________

Other Kinds of Numbers in Division Problems with Fractions

There are other kinds of numbers which can occur in division problems with fractions. Some problems require dividing a fraction by a whole number. To divide a fraction by a whole number, follow this handy rule.

A Handy Rule for Dividing a Fraction by a Whole Number

To divide a fraction by any whole number, except 0, first write the whole number over 1. Then divide according to the rule for division by a fraction.

$$\frac{2}{3} \div 6 = \frac{2}{3} \div \frac{6}{1} = \frac{2}{3} \times \frac{1}{6} = \frac{2}{18} = \frac{1}{9}$$

We have shown you how to divide a fraction by a whole number ($\frac{2}{3} \div 6$). We have also divided a whole number by a fraction ($6 \div \frac{2}{3}$). Let's review this problem to make the difference clear.

You can see that $6 \div \frac{2}{3}$ is DIFFERENT from $\frac{2}{3} \div 6$.

$6 \div \frac{2}{3} = 6 \times \frac{3}{2}$ (Turn the fraction we are dividing by upside down and multiply.)

Our problem is now $6 \times \frac{3}{2}$. If you remember how to multiply a whole number by a fraction, you will write $\frac{6}{1} \times \frac{3}{2} = \frac{18}{2} = 9$.

$\frac{2}{3} \div 6$ was $\frac{1}{9}$ $\qquad$ $6 \div \frac{2}{3}$ was 9

The order in which the numbers in a division problem are written makes a **big difference** in the answers.

Drill for Skill (XI)

1. $\frac{1}{2} \div 4 =$ ______________
2. $9 \div \frac{2}{3} =$ ______________
3. $\frac{7}{8} \div 3 =$ ______________
4. $10 \div \frac{1}{4} =$ ______________
5. $\frac{5}{8} \div 10 =$ ______________

Division Problems with Mixed Numbers

Some of the division problems we will be doing will have mixed numbers in them. To do a division problem which contains mixed numbers, follow this handy rule.

A Handy Rule for Dividing with Mixed Numbers

1. First change the mixed numbers into improper fractions.
2. Then follow the rules for dividing with fractions.

Example: $\frac{2}{3} \div 1\frac{1}{2} = \frac{2}{3} \div \frac{3}{2} = \frac{2}{3} \times \frac{2}{3} = \frac{4}{9}$

Drill for Skill (XII)

1. $1\frac{1}{2} \div 4 =$ ______________
2. $2\frac{1}{2} \div \frac{1}{4} =$ ______________
3. $1\frac{2}{3} \div 2\frac{3}{4} =$ ______________
4. $\frac{7}{28} \div 2\frac{1}{3} =$ ______________
5. $2\frac{1}{2} \div 6 =$ ______________
6. $6 \div 2\frac{1}{2} =$ ______________

Word Problems That Require Division with Fractions

Many word problems that require division with fractions sound much the same as word problems that require us to divide when we are working with whole numbers. For example, if something has been split into **equal** parts and we are asked

How big is each part?

How much will each receive?

How big is each person's share?

we **divide**. The key idea in these questions is **equal parts** or **shares**.

Questions that ask us how many times a smaller thing **is contained** in a larger thing also require us to divide. For example, if we asked how many quarter-pound burgers can be made from $1\frac{3}{4}$ pound of meat, we would really be asking how many times $\frac{1}{4}$ is contained in $1\frac{3}{4}$.

Questions that have the key word **per** in them often require division also. Be on the lookout to divide when you are asked to find how many somethings **per** something—like how many miles did she travel **per** hour, or how many words can he type **per** minute.

Now we will work out some examples of word problems that use the three types of key ideas we have mentioned.

First, let's try a problem that uses the idea of finding the size of each equal share. In this particular example, we will be dividing a fraction by a whole number. Imagine that you have $\frac{1}{2}$ box of peanuts ($\frac{1}{2}$ is your fraction). You are going to divide the peanuts equally among 3 monkeys (3 is your whole number). What would be each monkey's share?

Solution:

The words **divide equally** and the question, "What is **each** monkey's share," clearly signal division. In solving problems which use such words:

(a) First ask, "What are we dividing up?" We are dividing up $\frac{1}{2}$ box of peanuts. This number goes on the LEFT of the division sign. Put $\frac{1}{2}$ here: $\frac{1}{2} \div$

(b) Then ask, "How many shares or parts are there going to be?" In our problem, there are 3 monkeys, so there will be three equal shares. Put this number on the RIGHT of the division sign. Write: $\frac{1}{2} \div 3$

(c) Do the division:

$\frac{1}{2} \div 3 = \frac{1}{2} \div \frac{3}{1}$ (Write 3 as $\frac{3}{1}$) $= \frac{1}{2} \times \frac{1}{3} = \frac{1}{6}$

We are talking about boxes; so, each monkey should receive $\frac{1}{6}$ box.

Some Problems to Try

1. A relay race was to be run over a length of $2\frac{3}{4}$ kilometers. If 4 persons were on the relay team and each runner ran an equal amount of the total distance, how far would each person run? ____________

Now let's try a problem in which we are asked how many times a smaller thing is contained in a larger thing. In this particular example, we will be dividing a mixed number by a fraction. Let's return to our problem with the hamburgers. How many quarter-pound burgers can be made from $1\frac{3}{4}$ pounds of meat? Remember, the problem asks how many times the smaller thing ($\frac{1}{4}$ pound burger) is contained in the larger thing ($1\frac{3}{4}$ pounds meat). Our rule for solving these problems is very easy.

Divide the larger thing by the smaller thing.

larger thing		smaller thing
$1\frac{3}{4}$	$\div$	$\frac{1}{4}$

$= \frac{7}{4} \div \frac{1}{4}$ (Changing $1\frac{3}{4}$ into an improper fraction) $= \frac{7}{4} \times \frac{4}{1} = \frac{28}{4} = 7$

The answer is 7 burgers.

Try this problem.

2. Cathy had a small pond in her back yard, where she kept water turtles in the summer. The pond held 20 liters of water when filled. When summer came, the pond was dry, and Cathy began to fill it, using a watering can that held $2\frac{1}{2}$ liters. How many cans would she need to fill the pond?

____

Now let's look at a division problem which uses the idea of **per**. When you see the word **per**, it does not automatically mean you should divide. **Per** occurs in other types of problems besides division problems. Be careful. Think division only when you are asked to find out how many somethings **per** something. Here is the problem:

Problem:	Joe's father was test driving his new car to see how many miles it got per gallon. He drove it 10 miles and used $3/4$ gallon of gas. How many miles did the car get **per** gallon? ____________
Solution:	The question here is "How many miles per gallon"—a signal to divide. When you see **per** in a question which asks you to divide, always write what is **before** the word per on the LEFT of the division sign. For example, if the question asks, "How many **miles** PER gallon?" Write: miles ÷ gallons $10 \div 3/4 = 10 \times 4/3 = 10/1 \times 4/3 = 40/3 = 13\frac{1}{3}$ The answer is $13\frac{1}{3}$ miles.

Try this problem.

3. John went on a 2-day camping trip. If he spent $\$20\frac{1}{2}$, how many dollars did he spend per day?

Some Questions for You

As you read each question in the next set of exercises, look for the key ideas.

How much is each equal share?

How many equal parts are contained in the whole?

How many somethings **per** something?

Word Problems for Practice (XVIII)

1. Mr. Jackson took his two children to the movies. He gave them $\frac{1}{2}$ box of popcorn. If he asked the children to share the popcorn equally, how much popcorn should each child get?

   ____

2. The President of the Blastem Fireworks Company was having a $3/4$ hour meeting with his 6 top assistants. The president asked each of the assistants to discuss how they would sell the Company's new product—sparklers that shot off red, green, and white lights. If each person spoke an equal amount of time, how long would each person speak?

   ____

3. If you changed a \$20 bill into quarters, how many quarters would you get?

   ____

4. During the winter, Mrs. Benjamin feeds the birds during cold days. One day she put $1\frac{1}{2}$ pounds of sunflower seeds into her bird feeder that swung from the clothesline. There were 12 birds hanging around the feeder. If they all shared equally, how much seed would there be for each bird?

   ____

5. José wanted to swim 300 meters. How many times would he have to swim across a pool that was $33\frac{1}{3}$ meters long to accomplish this?

   ____

6. A student was reading a book in a foreign language. She had to use the dictionary a lot to look up words she didn't know, so her progress was slow. If she read $10\frac{2}{3}$ pages in 2 days, how many pages did she average reading per day?

   ____

7. In a wood-working class, the instructor cut a board $3\frac{8}{16}$ meters long into 6 equal parts. How long was each part?

   ____

8. In the school office there was a file cabinet with space large enough to hold 10 inches of files. If the files were stacked one on top of the other, how many files $\frac{1}{4}$ inch thick could fit into that space?

   ____

Name ______________________________

Date ______________________________

÷

The Wisdom of Solomon

Once there lived a man who had ten unruly children. His name was Solomon Small. Solomon was a poor man and it took a great effort and much sacrifice to save enough money to buy a bicycle for his children. Finally, the long-awaited day came and he presented a bright blue bicycle to his ten children. They gathered around him and he said, "Children, we have only one bicycle and there are ten of you. You will have to decide how to split up the use of the bicycle."

Immediately there was an argument. The oldest child said that he should use it most, because he was the oldest. The youngest child said he should use it the most, because he was the youngest. The ones in between said they should use it the most, because they were in between.

Finally Solomon said, "You shall split the use of it evenly: $^1/_{10}$ of the bicycle to each of you." The children nodded their heads. The oldest child then drew up a plan dividing 24 hours into tenths. However, he worked out the plan so he would use the bicycle after school while his brothers and sisters would spend most of their time riding the bike between midnight and 7:00 a.m. The idea did not go over too well. There was shouting, screaming, fist-fighting, and hair-pullinig. Finally, Solomon couldn't stand it any more. He left the room and switched on his radio, tuning in a rock band. He turned up the volume so loud that the sound vibrations cracked the plaster on the wall. Only then did he gain a feeling of peace and quiet.

The next day the oldest child came to Solomon. "I have the solution," he said, very sure of himself. "We will divide the bike itself into tenths. I will take the wheels, Jenny can take the handle bars, Al can have the tail light, and the rest of the kids can divide up the spokes."

Solomon stroked his chin while he considered the suggestion. Once again he gathered his children. He presented the idea to them and asked, "Do you all agree?" They all nodded their heads except little Bertram, who inquired, "Heh, Pop, how am I going to ride on spokes?"

Solomon replied, "Ah ha!" He gave the bike to Bertram and told the rest of the kids to go fly a kite—providing they could figure a way to share it.

Name ______________________________

Date ______________________________

Finding the Whole Thing When You Know a Part of It

ANOTHER TYPE OF PROBLEM THAT CAN BE SOLVED BY DIVIDING WITH FRACTIONS

We have already discussed key words that signal division. There is another type of problem you can solve by dividing with fractions. These problems give you some information about a part of something. For example, they may tell you:

A section of road is $\frac{3}{4}$ kilometer long.

Next, they tell you what fractional part of the whole road the section is. Let's say they tell you:

The section is $\frac{1}{2}$ of the whole road.

And they ask you:

HOW LONG IS THE WHOLE ROAD?

Does this sound difficult? Not really, if you know how to do it—and here's how.

A Handy Rule for Finding the Size of a Whole Thing When You Know the Size of a Fractional Part of It

1. First, ask "What is the information I am given about the part?" Usually, it will be "how big" the part is. In the question about the road which is described above, the section of road is $\frac{3}{4}$ kilometer long. In our instructions, we shall call this "the given part."
2. Next, ask "What fraction of the whole thing is the given part?" In the question about the road which is described above, the section of the road is $\frac{1}{2}$ the whole road.
3. Then divide as follows:

GIVEN PART ÷ THE FRACTION THE GIVEN PART IS OF THE WHOLE THING

Let's apply these 1-2-3 steps to our road problem.

1. The length of the section is $\frac{3}{4}$ kilometer long.
2. The section is $\frac{1}{2}$ the whole road.
3. $\frac{3}{4} \div \frac{1}{2} = \frac{3}{4} \times \frac{2}{1} = \frac{6}{4} = 1\frac{1}{2}$

Answer: the whole road is $1\frac{1}{2}$ kilometers long.

Name ______________________________

Date ______________________________

Reproducible

Here is a second example.

Example: Suppose you had a vegetable garden. Three quarters of an acre were planted with tomatoes. The tomatoes took up seven eights of the garden. How many acres were there in the total garden?

Solution: You are **given a fractional part** of a garden (the tomatoes), and you are asked for the size of the **whole** garden. Follow the 1, 2, 3 steps above.

1. The given part is $3/4$ acre of tomatoes.
2. The tomatoes are $7/8$ of the whole garden.
3. So divide $3/4$ by $7/8$:

$$3/4 \div 7/8 = 3/4 \times 8/7 = 24/28 = 6/7$$

The answer is $6/7$ acre.

Try this problem.

A Problem to Try

Jerry was sitting in Spanish class. He looked at the clock. The class had been underway now for $1/2$ hour. This was $1/3$ of the total time the class would last. For how much time was the class supposed to meet? In this problem

(a) What is the given part? ____________

(b) What fraction of the whole thing is the given part? ____________

(c) Now divide

given part ÷ fraction of the whole thing
(a) (b)

Your answer ____________

Word Problems for Practice (XIX)

1. Ellen's mother was sick, so Ellen decided to cook dinner for the family. She found the recipe she wanted and looked in the refrigerator. There was only $\frac{2}{3}$ cup of butter. This was $\frac{1}{2}$ of what the recipe called for. How much butter did the whole recipe call for?

   ____

2. If an unmanned space craft orbiting the earth completed $\frac{5}{9}$ of its total orbit in $\frac{3}{4}$ of an hour, how much time would a whole orbit take?

   ____

3. Julie went to the post office to mail a birthday present to her brother who was away at college. She had money for a half dollar's worth of stamps. The post office clerk said this amount would pay for only $\frac{1}{4}$ the postage she needed to mail the package. What was the cost of mailing the package?

   ____

4. At the beginning of winter, the gas station attendant checked the car to see how much antifreeze was needed. He poured $\frac{3}{4}$ liter of antifreeze into the car. As this was only $\frac{4}{5}$ of what the car actually needed, the attendant went to get more antifreeze. How much antifreeze had the car actually needed?

   ____

5. A woman was painting her living room. If it took $1\frac{1}{4}$ quarts of paint to paint $\frac{1}{3}$ of the room, how many quarts of paint would it take to paint the entire room?

   ____

6. The math teacher looked at the exam papers in despair. She threw up her hands. Nine of the students had failed the test. She exclaimed, "That's one third of the class." How many students were in the class?

   ____

7. For the family reunion, Grandma Spencer was roasting a turkey. She checked the meat thermometer after 3 hours and decided that the bird was one quarter done. If she were right, what is the total time that it took to cook the turkey?

   ____

8. It was election night. The votes were being counted. The mayor had only 50,000 votes. That was $\frac{1}{5}$ of what he thought he needed to win. How many votes did the mayor thing he needed to win?

   ____

Name ________________________________

Date ________________________________

÷

Reproducible

Dividing with Fractions

If you are a math buff, you will ask **why** this method for finding the whole thing works. Let's go back to the question of the tomatoes in the garden.

Here it is again:

Suppose you had a vegetable garden. Three quarters of an acre were planted with tomatoes. The tomatoes took up seven eights of the garden. How many acres were there in the total garden?

____

Well, think about it:

Solution: $\frac{7}{8}$ **of** the garden is tomatoes

$\frac{7}{8}$ **of** the garden = $\frac{3}{4}$ acre

$\mathbf{\frac{7}{8}}$ of the whole thing = $\frac{3}{4}$ acre

When we studied multiplication, we learned that a fractional part **of** the whole thing means the fractional part multiplied by the whole thing.

Therefore $\frac{7}{8}$ **of** the whole thing = $\frac{3}{4}$ acre
means $\frac{7}{8} \times$ the whole thing = $\frac{3}{4}$ acre.

We do not know the whole thing (the size of the garden).

So the question is $\frac{7}{8} \times$ WHAT = $\frac{3}{4}$ acre?

Difficult?

Well, think about something easier, like whole numbers. Think of an easy problem, like $2 \times$ WHAT = 6.

The answer is obviously 3, or $6 \div 2$.

So the answer to $\frac{7}{8} \times$ WHAT = $\frac{3}{4}$ must be $\frac{3}{4} \div \frac{7}{8} = \frac{3}{4} \times \frac{8}{7} = \frac{24}{28}$ which reduces to $\frac{6}{7}$.

We are talking about acres, so the answer is $\frac{6}{7}$ acres.

Name ______________________________

Date ______________________________

÷

Reproducible

Dividing with Fractions

Word Problem Review Test

This test will help you find out how well you learned and remembered the material you have covered so far. The test will include problems of all kinds. In answering the questions, you may have to use addition, subtraction, multiplication or division of fractions. As we have mixed up the problems, like shuffling a deck of cards, you will not be able to tell what kind of problem it is by the order in which it comes up. To solve the problems, read them carefully. Look for what the problem is asking you to do; then apply the skills you have learned.

1. If a car used $9\frac{1}{2}$ gallons of gas on the outward part of a trip and $8\frac{2}{3}$ gallons on the return part of the trip, how many gallons were used in all?

   ____

2. The great mirror of the huge reflecting telescope at Mount Palomar weighed $19\frac{3}{4}$ tons when originally cast. When the mirror was ground and polished, $5\frac{1}{4}$ tons of glass were removed. How much did the mirror weigh then?

   ____

3. During one week $\frac{1}{5}$ of the 800 students of the Edison Junior High School were out with the flu. How many students were not in school?

   ____

4. If it takes $\frac{3}{4}$ of an hour to cook $\frac{1}{4}$ of a roast, how long would it take to cook the entire roast (assuming that it cooks evenly)? ______________

5. In 1992, a stock sold for $22\frac{1}{4}$ dollars. In 1996, the same stock sold for $24\frac{1}{2}$ dollars. How much had the stock gained in value? ______________

6. As a work-study student in a community college, Joe was being paid 6 dollars each hour. One day, he worked $2\frac{1}{2}$ hours in the math department's office, where he answered the telephone. How much money did Joe earn?

   ____

7. The gas tank of Mrs. Chung's car was $\frac{1}{2}$ full. After she used the car for shopping, $\frac{1}{5}$ of this gas was used. What fraction of a tankful of gas was used during this shopping trip? ______________

8. One of the early rocket launchers in the U.S. space program (the Atlas-Centaur) could lift $6\frac{1}{2}$ tons into Earth's orbit. One of the later rockets (the Titan III-C) could lift 15 tons into orbit. What is the difference in the number of tons that the two rockets could raise into Earth orbit?

   ____

9. Gordon spent $\frac{3}{4}$ of an hour doing some of his homework. He spent $\frac{2}{3}$ of his time studying math and the rest of the time studying history. How much time did he spend studying math? ______________

10. Tom's hobby was woodworking. In looking through his supply of plywood, Tom found a sheet of oak $\frac{3}{16}$" thick, a sheet of birch $\frac{1}{8}$" thick and a sheet of knotty pine $\frac{3}{4}$" thick. What would be the thickness of the three sheets of plywood if they were combined? ____________

11. An office kept a petty cash fund. At the end of the year they decided to spend $\frac{1}{4}$ of the fund for a Christmas party and $\frac{2}{3}$ of the fund to buy presents for a needy family. What fraction of the petty cash was spent? ____________

12. Some junior high school students put on a puppet show to raise money for the Heart Fund. On the first day's performance they made 60 dollars. On the second day's performance they made $\frac{3}{4}$ of this amount. How much money did they make the second day? ____________

13. One third of a meter of snow fell in January. If this was $\frac{1}{5}$ of the total snowfall for the winter, how many meters of snow fell that winter? ____________

14. A surgeon made two incisions (cuts) into her patient during an operation. The first incision was $1\frac{3}{4}$" long. The second incision was $\frac{15}{16}$" long. How much longer was the first incision than the second? ____________

15. A scientist, who used only a paper and pencil, did some calculating in 5 seconds. His assistant, who used a computer, did the same problem in $\frac{1}{10,000}$ of that time. How long did it take his assistant who used the computer as a tool in helping do the problem? ____________

16. Inez was writing Christmas cards. When she had written 20 cards, she had finished $\frac{2}{3}$ of the number she had planned to send. How many cards did she plan to send? ____________

17. One night Jack didn't sleep well, because he was taking a trip in the morning and was very excited about it. He slept for $4\frac{1}{2}$ hours. This was only $\frac{3}{5}$ the amount of time he usually slept. How many hours did Jack usually sleep? ____________

18. Barbara had an accident while skiing and hurt her ankle. Her doctor told her to soak her ankle in hot water several times a day for a few days. In the beginning, Barbara soaked her ankle for $\frac{1}{3}$ of an hour. When the ankle felt better, she cut this time down to $\frac{1}{6}$ of an hour. By how much did she reduce the period of time she soaked her ankle? ____________

Advanced Problems That Require Two or More Different Operations

This chapter begins with a reminder to students to read all the way through any word problem to clearly identify what operations are needed and in what order they need to be done. The lessons include problems requiring addition and then subtraction, problems requiring multiplication and then subtraction, and problems requiring addition and then division (averages involving fractions). The chapter closes with special Brain Buster problems (with sample problems) and a quiz.

Answers

Word Problems for Practice XX

1. $1\frac{1}{4}$ in., **2.** \$2 million, **3.** 4 grams, **4.** $\frac{3}{20}$, **5.** \$$14\frac{1}{4}$, **6.** $1\frac{3}{4}$ mi., **7.** 4 c.

Word Problems for Practice XXI

1. \$45, **2.** \$$27\frac{1}{2}$, **3.** 1,200 km., **4.** $251\frac{1}{3}$ ft., $502\frac{2}{3}$ ft., **5.** 180 lbs., **6.** 8 students, **7.** \$8,200, **8.** 400 words, **9.** $1\frac{1}{5}$ hrs., **10 a.** \$6, \$24, **b.** \$5, \$15, **c.** \$39.

Word Problems for Practice XXII

1. $4\frac{2}{5}$ m., **2.** $5\frac{1}{2}$ in., **3.** \$50, **4. a.** 2 hrs., **b.** 9 hrs., **c.** 7 hrs., **Measuring the Waves:** 12 in.

Brain Busters

1. 20 people, **2.** 24,000 copies, **3.** 36 girls, **4.** 12 points, **5.** $\frac{4}{15}$

Name ______________________________

Date ______________________________

Reproducible

Advanced Problems That Require Two or More Different Operations

This is a chapter for the person who likes a challenge. In the earlier chapters, you were able to solve a problem by first deciding what type of arithmetical operation you needed to use—addition or subtraction or multiplication or division—and then going ahead and doing that operation. However, many arithmetic problems require two or more steps. Sometimes you must add, then subtract, as you do in checking your bank balance. Sometimes you must first add, then multiply. At other times, you might use any two, three, or four of the operations that you have mastered. The main thing to remember in solving such problems is to:

1. First, think out the steps you will need to use **before** you start working the problem.
2. Then take these steps, one at a time, carefully.

There are many kinds of problems that use two or more different operations of arithmetic. We have chosen to show just a few of these types of problems in detail—the kinds we think might be important to you in everyday life. We have also added a few very difficult problems which you might have fun trying to solve. These we have called the "Brain Busters."

Problems in Which You Must First Add, Then Subtract

Bill and Sally Taylor were giving a party. They had $3\frac{1}{2}$ hours in which to get ready. First they decided to clean their apartment. This took $1\frac{1}{4}$ hours. Then they went shopping at the supermarket. This took another $\frac{3}{4}$ hour. After cleaning and shopping, how much time did they have to get ready for the party? ____________

What is the problem asking you to do?

It's asking you to find something that's left.

This means you have to **subtract**.

You have to subtract—but what are you going to subtract from?

That's a cinch. The $3\frac{1}{2}$ hours they have to get ready for the party.

Excellent. Now what are you going to subtract?

Name ______________________________

Date ______________________________

Reproducible

Advanced Problems That Require Two or More Different Operations

Bill and Sally have already done two things—cleaning and shopping. If you find the **total** time they spent cleaning and shopping—THAT WOULD TELL YOU HOW MUCH TIME THEY HAVE ALREADY SPENT. That's what you would subtract—the total time they have already spent—TO FIND OUT HOW MUCH TIME IS LEFT. The problem calls for two steps.

Step A	**Step B**
Add to find the total amount of time the Taylors have already used. $1\frac{1}{4}$ hours cleaning $\frac{3}{4}$ hour shopping $1\frac{1}{4} + \frac{3}{4} = \frac{5}{4} + \frac{3}{4} = \frac{8}{4} = 2$ The total time is 2 hours.	**Subtract** the total time the Taylors have used (2 hours) from the amount of time they had originally to get ready for the party ($3\frac{1}{2}$ hours.) That's $3\frac{1}{2}$ hours minus 2 hours. That's $3\frac{1}{2} - 2 = \frac{7}{2} - \frac{2}{1} = \frac{7}{2} - \frac{4}{2} = \frac{3}{2} = 1\frac{1}{2}$. The answer is $1\frac{1}{2}$ hours.

We have now worked a problem that called for two operations to solve it, addition and subtraction. In this problem, we had to first add two small parts to come up with a larger one. Only then could we subtract to find what remained.

Word Problems for Practice (XX)

1. The weatherman predicted that 10 inches of snow would fall during the day. In the morning it snowed $5\frac{1}{2}$ inches and in the early afternoon another $3\frac{1}{4}$ inches. How much more snow would have to fall to reach the amount the weatherman predicted? ______________
2. The owner of a professional baseball team told his general manager to sign up some free-agent ball players. He told the general manager that he could spend 10 million dollars on contracts. The general manager signed up infielder Hal Zigbog for $2\frac{1}{4}$ million dollars, outfielder George Gothic for $1\frac{1}{4}$ million dollars, and pitcher Jimmy Jinx for $4\frac{1}{2}$ million dollars. How many million dollars were still left to be spent? ______________
3. In chemistry class, Beth needed $18\frac{1}{2}$ grams of calcium to do an experiment. She found three small bottles that contained calcium. The first bottle contained $5\frac{1}{2}$ grams, the second $4\frac{1}{2}$ grams, and the third $4\frac{1}{2}$ grams. If she combined the calcium from the three bottles, by how much would she be under the amount of calcium she needed for the experiment? ______________
4. When Miguel started college, he got a part-time job typing to help pay his expenses. Three fifths of what he earned was used for school expenses, $\frac{1}{4}$ of his earnings was used for clothes and the remaining amount was put into a savings account. What part of his earnings went into his savings account? ______________

5. Mr. Colby went shopping at the supermarket. He had a twenty-dollar bill in his wallet. He bought some meat which cost $3\frac{1}{4}$ dollars and some fresh vegetables which cost $2\frac{1}{2}$ dollars. How much change would Mr. Colby get back from his twenty-dollar bill? ____________

Be careful on this one!

6. Bill decided to ride his bicycle to strengthen his legs for football season. His first day's goal was to ride 4 miles. In the morning he rode $2\frac{1}{2}$ miles. In the afternoon, he rode $3\frac{1}{4}$ miles. By how much was he over his goal? ____________ (Hint: Find out how many miles he actually rode. Then subtract how much he planned to ride from this.)

7. A recipe called for $1\frac{1}{2}$ cups of red peppers. The chef was daydreaming when he put the peppers in. First, he put in $1\frac{1}{2}$ cups, then $2\frac{1}{2}$ cups and finally another $1\frac{1}{2}$ cups. How many more cups of peppers did he put in than he was supposed to? ____________

Problems That Require You to First Multiply, Then Subtract

If you glance back at Chapter 5 where we were multiplying whole numbers by fractions (pages 64 through 67), you'll see problems like this:

Problem:	A sweater selling for \$15 has been reduced by $\frac{1}{3}$. By now many dollars has the price been reduced?
	In solving the problem, we multiplied \$15 by $\frac{1}{3}$.
	$15 \times \frac{1}{3} = \frac{15}{3} = 5$
	The answer is \$5.

By multiplying, you found that the sweater had been marked down \$5. But suppose the problem were worded, "A sweater originally selling for \$15 has been reduced by $\frac{1}{3}$. What is the new price? ____________

This is an important question, because just knowing you can save \$5 isn't enough if you are actually shopping. You want to know how much you are actually going to pay. To find this out, you have to do a second step.

If the sweater costs \$15 and it has been reduced by \$5, you want to know **what remains** to be paid. and **what remains**, of course, means **subtract**.

Original price	\$15
– Amount reduced	\$5 (your savings)
New price	\$10 (what you must pay)

So to solve the above problem, we must go through two steps:

A. **Multiply** the whole number (15) by the fraction ($\frac{1}{3}$).

B. **Subtract** the answer (5) from the original whole number (15).

Here is another example on multiplying whole numbers by fractions.

Example: Suppose you were driving your car on a trip of 180 miles. You look at the map and you can see that you have gone $\frac{1}{3}$ of the distance. How many miles have you already traveled? __________

In solving the problem you multiply 180 miles × $\frac{1}{3}$ and come up with the answer of 60 miles. Fine, you know you've gone 60 miles. But suppose the last line of the question were worded, "How far do you still have to go?"

Solving this problem requires you to take a second step. That second step asks you to find the **distance yet to be traveled** or WHAT REMAINS.

your whole trip	180 miles
you have already gone	– 60 miles
left to go	120 miles

You subtract, of course.

The two steps taken to solve this problem are:

A. **Multiply** the whole number (180) by the fraction ($\frac{1}{3}$) **to find the distance already traveled**.

B. **Subtract** the distance already traveled (60 miles) from the distance of the whole trip (180 miles) **to find the distance yet to be traveled**.

Word Problems for Practice (XXI)

1. Randy was starting his first year at a community college. He needed to buy a history textbook. The usual cost of the book was $60. Because the book had been slightly damaged in handling, the book was priced at "$\frac{1}{4}$ off." For how much did the book now sell? ______________

2. After Christmas, the Jenkins Camera Store had a sale. A new instant camera which had been selling for $55 had been reduced by $\frac{1}{2}$. What was the new selling price? ______________

3. Nancy lived in central Canada and was attending college in Toronto. The college was 1800 kilometers from her hometown. When Nancy drove home for summer vacation, she drove $\frac{1}{3}$ of the distance on her first day's travel. How many kilometers did she have yet to drive? ______________

4. The Loch Ness Monster is said to be a mysterious creature that lives in a deep lake in northern Scotland. According to one person who claimed to have seen it, it was a green creature with webbed feet and a 12-foot tail. The lake is said to be 754 feet at its deepest. If the creature dove to a depth $\frac{1}{3}$ of the way to the deepest point, how far would it be from the lake's surface? ______________ How much farther would the monster have to travel to reach the deepest point in the lake? ______________

5. Felix weighed himself on the bathroom scale. The scale read an even 200 pounds. The next day Felix went on a diet. During the next three months he lost $\frac{1}{10}$ of that weight. How much did he then weigh? ______________

6. Twenty students tried out for the school cheerleading squad. After one week, $\frac{3}{5}$ of the students were cut. How many students were left? ______________

7. A woman bought a new car that cost $12,300. After one year of use, the value of the car had dropped by $\frac{1}{3}$. What was the car worth after one year? ______________

8. Ron was writing a term paper for English class. His subject was "The Original Olympic Games—the Ones Held in Ancient Greece." Ron was supposed to write 1,000 words. After he had completed $\frac{3}{5}$ of the paper, he took a break and went out to play football. How many words did he still need to write? ______________

9. Mr. Barry was waiting at the airport for a connecting flight that would take him home. He had three hours to kill. He took out some work from his briefcase. He thought that this would fill $\frac{3}{5}$ of his time. Then he thought he would read a magazine for the remaining time. How much time would remain for him to read the magazine? ______________

CHALLENGE QUESTION

10. You are going into a store where there is a big sale. "You buy a sweater that originally sold for $30 and is now $\frac{1}{5}$ off. Then you buy one pair of jeans that originally sold for $20 and are now reduced by $\frac{1}{4}$." How much money do you spend altogether? ______________ (As this is a BIG problem, we'll give you some help.)

    (a) Figure out the savings on the sweater. ______________
    Figure out the new price of the sweater. ______________

    (b) Figure out the savings on the jeans. ______________
    Figure out the new price of the jeans. ______________

    (c) Now ask, what is the total cost? (Just add the new prices for the sweater and the jeans.) ______________

Name ______________________________

Date ______________________________

Reproducible

Advanced Problems That Require Two or More Different Operations

Finding Averages When Fractions Are Involved

Here you must use addition and division.

Have you ever figured out **averages of** whole numbers? Perhaps you have figured out batting averages for a baseball team or maybe you have computed your average expenses for a week. You may remember that when you figured out averages, you first added up the individual items, then divided this sum by the number of items.

For example, if you spent \$10 the first week, \$15 the second week, \$5 the third week, your average weekly spending would be found using these steps:

A. First **add** \$10 + \$15 + \$5 = \$30.

B. Then **divide** \$30 ÷ 3 (because you are dealing with three weeks).

The answer is \$10.

Sometimes your items may include fractions or mixed numbers. When this happens, you find the average in the same manner. Let's suppose you spent $10\frac{1}{4}$ dollars the first week, $15\frac{3}{4}$ dollars the second week, 5 dollars the third week, and 9 dollars the fourth week. What would be your average weekly spending?

A. **Add** $\$10\frac{1}{4} + \$15\frac{3}{4} + \$5 + \$9$

$= \frac{41}{4} + \frac{63}{4} + \frac{5}{1} + \frac{9}{1}$

$= \frac{41}{4} + \frac{63}{4} + \frac{20}{4} + \frac{36}{4}$

$= \frac{160}{4} = 40$

Your total spending is \$40.

B. Divide the sum of \$40 by 4.

40 ÷ 4 = 10

Your average spending is 10 dollars per week.

Name ______________________________

Date ______________________________

Reproducible

Advanced Problems That Require Two or More Different Operations

Word Problems for Practice (XXII)

Here are a few problems which ask you to find averages. You will need to add fractions in Step A, then divide by a **whole number** in Step B.

1. Delores was trying out for the school track team. She was practicing broad jumps. She made 3 jumps. The jumps were $4\frac{1}{2}$ meters, $4\frac{2}{5}$ meters, and $4\frac{3}{10}$ meters. What was the average length of her jump? ____________

2. In the Pacific Northwest, it rains a lot in the winter. In one town, it rained $4\frac{1}{2}$" in December, $5\frac{2}{3}$" inches in January, 6" in February, and $5\frac{5}{6}$" in March. What was the average monthly rainfall during this period of time? ____________

3. Alice's Aunt Agatha left Alice some stock in a gold-mining company. Every morning Alice got out the stock market page from the newspaper to see how her stock was doing. On Monday it was priced at $50\frac{3}{4}$ dollars; on Tuesday, $49\frac{1}{2}$ dollars; on Wednesday, $48\frac{1}{4}$ dollars; on Thursday, $49\frac{1}{2}$ dollars, and on Friday, 52 dollars. What was the average price for the stock during the week? ____________

4. Mr. Sterling had a very demanding job. One week things got very tough and he was under a lot of pressure. He began to have trouble sleeping. On Monday night, he slept $3\frac{1}{3}$ hours; on Tuesday night, he slept $1\frac{2}{3}$ hours; and on Wednesday night he slept only 1 hour all night. On Thursday, he went to a doctor, who gave him some medicine to help him sleep and told him to take a few days off. The treatment worked. On the next three days following his visit to the doctor, Mr. Sterling slept 7 hours, $9\frac{1}{2}$ hours, and $10\frac{1}{2}$ hours, and said he felt a lot better.

   (a) What was the average amount of sleep Mr. Sterling got for the three nights before he went to the doctor? ____________

   (b) What was the average amount of sleep Mr. Sterling got for the three nights after he went to the doctor? ____________

   (c) Let's try carrying this out to a **third** step. How much more sleep did Mr. Sterling average after seeing the doctor than before? ____________

Name ______________________________

Date ______________________________

Reproducible

Advanced Problems That Require Two or More Different Operations

Measuring the Waves

Who would want to measure the height of waves as they hit the shoreline on the beach? Well, Lisa and Brian did. They were kids with a lot of curiosity and with a lively interest in nature and science. They wondered how high the waves got at different times during the day. To find out, they stuck a pole firmly into the sand and observed and measured the height the water reached as it washed against the pole. Here are the measurements that Lisa and Brian made during a short time.

$12\frac{1}{2}$ inches	$13\frac{1}{2}$ inches
14 inches	9 inches.
11 inches	

What is the average of their measurements? ______________

To make their comparisons with other times of the day, Lisa and Brian knew that they would have to place the pole in the same spot on the beach. To mark that spot, they built a sand castle and hoped it wouldn't wash away.

A MIND-READING TRICK TO PLAY ON YOUR FRIENDS

Tell your friends to follow these five instructions carefully and you will always be able to guess their final result.

1. Think of a fraction. __________
2. Multiply that fraction by 2. __________
3. Add 10. __________
4. Divide by 2. __________
5. Subtract the fraction you originally thought of in Step 1 from your answer in Step 4. __________

You should first try this trick several times yourself using any fractions that you wish. You will see that the final result will always be 5. When you try this trick on your friends, give them a knowing look after they have completed the five steps above, and say, "Your final result must be 5."

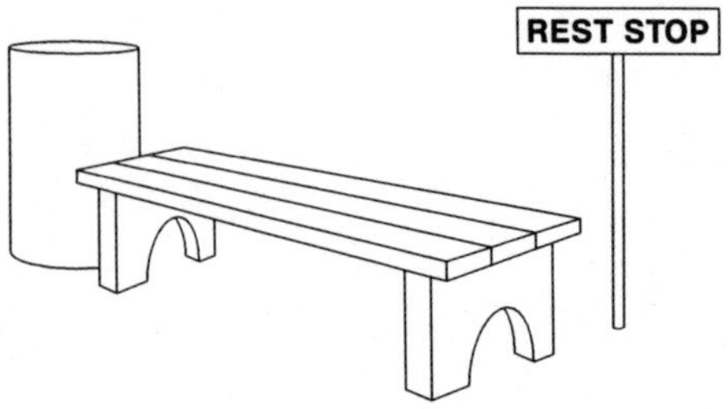

Name ______________________________

Date ______________________________

Reproducible

Advanced Problems That Require Two or More Different Operations

And Now, on to Brain Busters!

Here are the rules. We will give you a number of difficult problems to solve. Each time we will first show you how to solve a sample problem that is very much like the one you will have to solve. First study the sample problem; then try to solve your problem.

If you get the problem right, you get a certain number of points. The harder the problem, the more points you get.

The Prizes
Gold Medal—100 total points
Silver Medal—70 total points
Bronze Medal—30 total points

Brain Buster No. 1 Sample Problem

Bill had $600 in his savings account at the bank. One weekend he decided to go to the beach. He withdrew $\frac{1}{3}$ of his savings from the bank before driving to the beach. By the time the weekend was over, he spent $\frac{3}{4}$ of the money he took out of the bank. How much money did he spend?

The question is "How much money did Bill spend? "To answer it, you don't really have to 'BUST YOUR BRAIN'—only exercise your brain muscle. Just

(a) read the problem carefully,

(b) look for clues,

(c) remember your key phrases.

Bill spent a fractional part of the money he took out of the bank.

To find a fractional part of something, you must multiply.

<u>Step A</u>

Bill spent $\frac{3}{4}$ **of** the money he took out of the bank

OR $\frac{3}{4} \times$ the money he took out of the bank

How much money did he take out of the bank? ______________

$\frac{1}{3}$ **of** $600

$$\frac{1}{3} \times \$600 = \frac{1}{3} \times \frac{\$600}{1} = \frac{\$600}{3} = \$200$$

<u>Step B</u>

So, we see Bill spent $\frac{3}{4}$ **OF** $200 he took out of the bank.

$$\frac{3}{4} \times \$200 = \frac{3}{4} \times \frac{200}{1} = \frac{600}{4} = 150$$

Your answer is $150.

• If you get this right, you get 10 points.

Five hundred people applied for a program for space training. One twentieth of the people were accepted. After a year's training, $^{8}/_{10}$ of the people who were accepted were still in the program. How many people were still in the program? ____________

Brain Buster No. 2 Sample Problem

A baseball player hit 20 home runs in his first season. In his second season, he increased the number of his home runs by $^{2}/_{5}$. How many home runs did he hit in his second year? __________

Solution:

The question is "How many home runs did the baseball player hit the second season?"

LOOK FOR CLUES!

The second season, he **increased** his home runs by $^{2}/_{5}$. Therefore, the second season, he had MORE home runs that the first season.

Remember the KEY PHRASES . . .

If something is **increased by a fraction, multiply** that fraction times what you had before the increase and you will find the increase.

We started with 20 home runs in our problem; the increase would be

$$^{2}/_{5} \times 20 = {}^{2}/_{5} \times {}^{20}/_{1} = {}^{40}/_{5} \text{ or } 8.$$

We know the ballplayer had 20 home runs the first season. In the second season he hit 8 more home runs. If we take his old figure 20 and add the increase 8, this sum will give us his new home run total.

The answer is 28 home runs.

• If you get this right, you get 20 points.

The first issue of a new magazine, *Talking with the Stars of T.V. and Screen*, sold 20,000 copies. Sales for the second issue were $^{1}/_{5}$ greater than the first issue. How many copies were sold the second issue? ____________

Brain Buster No. 3 Sample Problem

Mrs. Stevens wants to plant 20 good tomato plants in her garden. She believes that some of the plants she plans to put into the ground may not do well. She thought about last year's garden and figured that 1 out of 5 of her new plants might not do well. So she decided to plant some extra tomato plants. If she is sure that $\frac{1}{5}$ of the plants may not do well, how many tomato plants should she put into the ground to get 20 good plants? ____________

Solution:

Step A

Mrs. Stevens **wants plants that do well**.

If $\frac{1}{5}$ do poorly, what fraction do well?

Remember the rule on page 56 for finding the missing fractional part?

If we know a fractional part of something, to find the **other** fractional part, subtract the fractional part we know from 1.

If we know $\frac{1}{5}$ of the tomato plants do poorly,

$$1 - \frac{1}{5} = \frac{1}{1} - \frac{1}{5} = \frac{5}{5} - \frac{1}{5} = \frac{4}{5} \text{ do well.}$$

This arithmetic shows that

$\frac{4}{5}$ of the tomato plants do well.

Step B

The question asks, How many tomatoes should be planted in the **whole** patch to get 20 good plants?"

We have information **about a fractional part of a whole and are asked to find the whole**. You've done this before. Turn back to page 80 and review the 1, 2, 3 steps we used to solve such problems.

1. There are 20 plants in the good part of the tomato patch.
2. The good part is $\frac{4}{5}$ of the whole tomato patch.
3. To find how many plants are in the WHOLE tomato patch, DIVIDE:

$$20 \div \frac{4}{5} = 20 \times \frac{5}{4} = \frac{20}{1} \times \frac{5}{4} = \frac{100}{4} = 25$$

Answer: Mrs. Stevens should plant 25 tomato plants.

- If you get this right, you get 30 points.

The director of the choir at Trinity Girls' School liked to have at least 30 girls in the choir. She knew from experience that $\frac{1}{6}$ of the girls would probably drop out during the school year because of other interests. How many girls would she probably need in the choir to make sure that she would have 30 during the school year? ____________

Name ______________________________

Date ______________________________

Reproducible

Advanced Problems That Require Two or More Different Operations

Brain Buster No. 4 Sample Problem

Madison High School had a contest for its students to see who could write the best short stories. Two hundred forty dollars in prize money was donated by the city newspaper. Two-thirds of the total prize money was given to the winner, while the second and third place finishers each received $\frac{1}{2}$ of what was left. How much money did the second and third place winners each receive?

____

Solution:

The question asks, "How much money did the second and third place winners each receive?

Step A

1. We know that each of them received $\frac{1}{2}$ of what was left after the winner was given her prize.
2. The winner's prize was $\frac{2}{3}$ OF \$240 = $\frac{2}{3} \times \frac{\$240}{1} = \frac{\$480}{3}$ = \$160

Step B

The total prize money minus the winner's prize equals what was left.

\$240 (total prize money) – \$160 (winner's prize money) = \$80 (what was left)

Step C

The second and third place winners each received HALF of what was left.

$\frac{1}{2}$ OF \$80 = $\frac{1}{2} \times$ \$80 = $\frac{1}{2} \times \frac{\$80}{1}$ = \$40

- If you get this right, you get 40 points.

The City College basketball team won a very important basketball game 72 to 71. During the game, the coach played only 5 players. The point guard set up the plays and didn't score at all. The center scored half of the points. The remaining three players each scored the same number of points. How many points did each of these three players score? ____________

Brain Buster No. 5 Sample Problem

A famous singer agreed to give a concert at Oldtown Community College. Three quarters of the tickets were sold on the first day of sales. One half of the remaining tickets were sold the very next day. What fraction of the tickets were not yet sold? ____________

Solution:

The question asks, "What fraction of the tickets **were not sold** at the end of the second day?" But that depends on what fraction were sold the first day.

So—**go back to Day 1**. Draw some pictures to keep track of what was sold and what was not sold each day.

Think of all the tickets being thrown into a basket which holds them exactly.

Day 1 Tickets

$\frac{3}{4}$ Sold

? Not Sold

End Day 1

$\frac{1}{4}$ left

Remember our Handy Rule?

If we know a fractional part of something and we are asked to find the fractional part of the thing that is left, we subtract the fractional part we know from 1: 1 – fractional part we know.

This means that at the end of Day 1:

$1 - \frac{3}{4} = \frac{1}{1} - \frac{3}{4} = \frac{4}{4} - \frac{3}{4} = \frac{1}{4}$ of the tickets are left!

End Day 1: $\frac{1}{4}$ left

Begin Day 2:

The second day $\frac{1}{2}$ **of** those left were sold. What's left? Look at the picture we just drew. $\frac{1}{4}$ is left. So, on day 2, $\frac{1}{2}$ of $\frac{1}{4}$ were sold.

If you know the fractional part of the total tickets sold, you can subtract this from 1 using the handy rule that will tell you how many tickets are left.

A. What fractional part of the tickets was sold in all? That's $\frac{3}{4}$ on the first day and $\frac{1}{8}$ on the second:

$\frac{3}{4} + \frac{1}{8}$. That's the same as $\frac{6}{8} + \frac{1}{8}$ which equals $\frac{7}{8}$.

B. Subtract this from 1. $1 - \frac{7}{8} = \frac{1}{8}$. So $\frac{1}{8}$ of the tickets have not yet been sold.

- If you get this right, you get 50 points.

Ms. Bristol was an assistant to the president of a large company. She spent $\frac{3}{5}$ of every day in meetings. One third of her remaining time, she spent dictating letters and reports. What fraction of her work time did she have left for other things? ______________

Fun and Games with Fractions

Teacher Notes

This chapter contains four fun and unusual problems involving probability and chance.

Answers

Coin Experiment

100, 100

Die Experiment

$\frac{1}{6}$, $\frac{1}{6}$, $\frac{1}{6}$; first column would stay the same, second would change

The Chaos Game

$\frac{1}{3}$

Name ______________________________

Date ______________________________

Reproducible

Fun and Games with Fractions

There are many interesting things in mathematics that you will probably learn more about as you continue to explore and study. Here, we will show you how to have fun using some of these ideas, without studying complicated theory. Your knowledge of fractions will help you understand these ideas.

Have you ever heard the phrase that something "will *probably* happen?" This phrase is related to the word "probability" in mathematics. "Probability" does not tell us what will happen; rather, probability helps us make educated guesses about how likely it is that something will happen. Probability tells us what we might expect.

Coin Experiment

To give you some idea of how probability tells us what to expect, let's experiment. Our experiment will be tossing a penny. What are the possibilities for our coin when it lands? There are only two possible outcomes. The penny could show heads when it lands or it could show tails.

The list of all possible outcomes of an experiment is called "the sample space." In our experiment, the sample space is {Heads, Tails}.

What fraction of the sample space is heads? $\frac{1}{2}$

What fraction of the sample space is tails? $\frac{1}{2}$

The fraction of the sample space that is heads is called "the probability of heads." The fraction of the sample space that is tails is called "the probability of heads." This means that if we do our experiment many times, a good, educated guess is that $\frac{1}{2}$ of our results will be heads. In the same way, $\frac{1}{2}$ is the probability of tails. This means that if we do our experiment many times, a good, educated guess is that $\frac{1}{2}$ of our results will be tails.

Let's play with this idea. Make a chart. Label one column "Heads." Label the other column "Tails."

Heads	Tails

Now, toss a coin 100 times. Each time you toss, make a mark in the heads column if the coin lands heads. Make a mark in the tails column, if you get tails.

How many heads does your heads column show? The number that you would expect is $\frac{1}{2} \times 100 = 50$. This does not mean that you got 50. Did you get close to 50 heads? 50 heads is only an educated guess about the number of heads to expect.

How many tails did you get? Is the number of tails you got close to your educated guess $\frac{1}{2} \times 100$?

What if you tossed a coin 200 times? How many heads would you expect? How many tails would you expect?

Try this coin tossing experiment with your friends. Compare your results.

Die Experiment

In some of your board games, such as Monopoly™, you may have used dice, those little cubes with dots on them. Dice can also be bought in many stores that sell games.

Here we are going to work with only one of the dice. One of the dice is called a "die." If we toss a die, there are six different ways that it can land. It can land so that the face with one dot appears on top, or the face with two dots appears on top, or the face with three dots appears on top, or the face with four dots appears on top, or the face with five dots appears on top, or the face with six dots appears on top. Our sample space for the experiment tossing a die has six different possibilities in it. This sample space is shown below:

The fraction of the sample space that has one dot on top is $\frac{1}{6}$. Therefore, the probability of one dot appearing on top is $\frac{1}{6}$. Can you guess the probability of two dots appearing on top? The fraction of our sample space that shows two dots on top is also $\frac{1}{6}$; so, the probability of two dots appearing on top is also $\frac{1}{6}$. What is the probability of 3 dots appearing on top? _______ How about 4 dots? _______ Five dots? _______ Six dots? _______.

If your die hasn't been imbalanced in some way (like maybe your dog's chewing a corner out of it), when you toss your die, each of the numbers of dots 1, 2, 3, 4, 5, 6 has the same probability ($\frac{1}{6}$) of appearing on the top face. This means that if you toss your die many times, a good guess is that $\frac{1}{6}$ of your tosses will show each of the numbers of dots 1, 2, 3, 4, 5, 6 on the top face.

Now, we are ready to experiment. Toss your die many times; let's say 96 times. We don't know what will happen. Let's see what happens. Complete the chart below for your experiment.

Good, Educated Guess for the number of Times You Will Get	How Many Times You Actually Got
1 dot on top	
2 dots on top	
3 dots on top	
4 dots on top	
5 dots on top	
6 dots on top	

Were your educated guesses close to what you actually got? If you did this experiment again, which column of your chart would stay the same? _______ Which column of your chart would you expect to change? _______

Why It's so Hard to Win the Jackpot

Does your state have a game such as a lottery in which people buy chances to win a big payoff? Have you ever wondered why it's so hard to win? Try our game, and you'll understand.

Imagine that each time you play this game, you have to buy a ticket for $1, as people do in many places when they play the lottery.

To win the jackpot, toss a die four times.

If your first number is a 4, and your second number is a 1, and your third number is a 2, and your fourth number is a 5, you win the jackpot!

Remember, that to win the jackpot, you must hit these numbers in **exactly** the order they are listed here

4 1 2 5.

All right? Toss the die to see if you get a 4. If you didn't get 4 dots on the top face, you struck out. You lost! What were your chances of getting a 4? One out of 6, or a probability of $\frac{1}{6}$.

If you didn't get a 4, keep trying until you get a 4. Each time you try, please remember that you must first buy a ticket which costs $1. When you do get a 4, toss the die again to try for the next number in the row, which is a 1. Did you get a 1? No, well, too bad. You lost. What were your chances of getting a 1? One out of 6. Your probability of getting a 1 was, therefore, $\frac{1}{6}$.

Mathematicians have calculated that the probability of getting the four numbers 4 1 2 5 in exactly the order in which they appear in the row is $\frac{1}{6} \times \frac{1}{6} \times \frac{1}{6} \times \frac{1}{6}$ or $\frac{1}{1,296}$. That means that you do not know whether you will ever get the numbers in the row; however, an educated guess is that if you played this game 1,296 times, you might hit the jackpot once. Imagine how much money you could throw away as you tossed a die in hopes that you would hit the jackpot. Now, try this game as many times as you want to convince yourself how hard it really is.

The Chaos Game

To play this game, you will need some friends. Each of them should have a piece of "see-through" paper (for example, tracing paper) with a copy of this triangle drawn on it. Just trace a copy of this triangle on each of your pieces of paper.

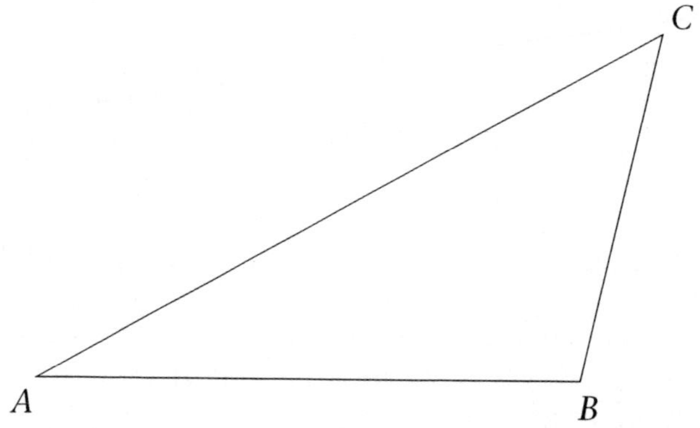

Each of you will also need a ruler to measure distances, as well as a die to toss.

Here are the rules of the game. This is what each of you should do. First, hold your pencil in the air just above the triangle you drew on your "see-through" paper. Now, close your eyes, and let the tip of your pencil fall within the triangle. Put a dark dot on the point inside the triangle that your pencil touched.

Now, roll a die. You might get a 1 or a 2 or a 3 or a 5 or a 6.

If you get a 1 or a 2, move halfway from your initial dot toward point *A* and put a dark dot there.

If you get a 3 or a 4, move halfway from your initial dot toward point *B* and put a dark dot there.

If you get a 5 or a 6, move halfway from your initial dot toward point *C* and put a dark dot there.

NOW, LET'S DO THE FOLLOWING AGAIN AND AGAIN AND AGAIN, . . . until you get tired.

ROLL THE DIE

If you get a 1 or a 2, move halfway from your last dot toward point *A* and put a dark dot there.

If you get a 3 or a 4, move halfway from your last dot toward point *B* and put a dark dot there.

If you get a 5 or a 6, move halfway from your last dot toward point *C* and put a dark dot there.

Each time you roll the die, there are 2 possibilities out of 6 that you will move toward point *A*. So, $\frac{2}{6}$ or $\frac{1}{3}$ of the time is a good guess that you will move toward point *A*. Each time you roll the die, there are 2 possibilities out of 6 that you will move toward point *B*. So, $\frac{1}{3}$ of the time is a good guess that you will be moving toward point *B*. How much of the time, would you expect to be moving toward point *C*? ________

How is your picture looking? Do you see any interesting patterns forming? When we work with probability, we are really making educated guesses about what will happen if we do something many, many times. In the chaos game, you need lots of dots to do this. That's why we asked you to work together with your friends—so that you could get many dots.

Here is what to do. Take all of the pictures that you made. Place your triangles exactly on top of each other and hold them up to a window. Do you see an interesting pattern forming by everybody's dots when your triangles are placed on top of each other?

When the chaos game is played many, many times with the help of a computer the beautiful picture that emerges from the dots looks something like the one below. Don't be disappointed if your picture doesn't measure up to this one. A computer doesn't get tired. Besides, you probably want to do things other than draw dots.

The picture below is made up of a triangle with other triangles inside it. If you look at the big triangle carefully, you will see that the triangle is really a miniature copy of the whole picture. Are you curious about the name given to pictures which are made up a miniatures of themselves? If so, they are called "fractals."

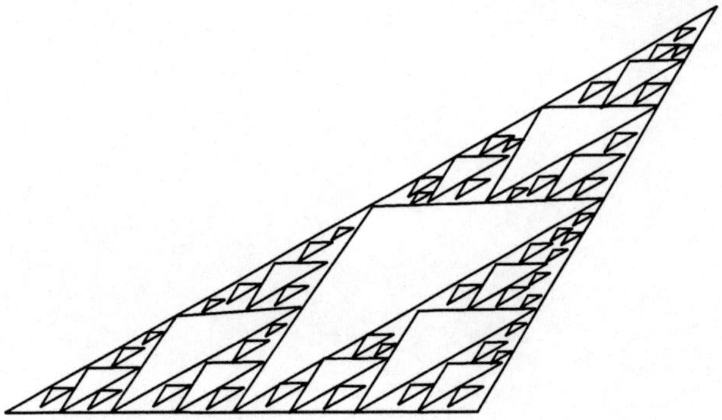

Appendices

Teacher Notes

The appendices offer another way to add mixed numbers, another way to subtract mixed numbers, and a shortcut for some multiplications.

Appendix A

ANOTHER WAY TO ADD MIXED NUMBERS

This is a useful way to add mixed numbers when the whole number parts are large.

1. Write the figures you are adding one above the other.
2. Then add the fractions. If this sum is an improper fraction, change it into a mixed number.
3. Next add the whole numbers.
4. Finally, add the sum found in Step 2 to the sum found in Step 3.

Example: a) Find $22\frac{1}{4} + 1\frac{1}{8}$

Solution:

$$\begin{array}{r} 22\frac{1}{4} \\ +\ 1\frac{1}{8} \\ \hline \end{array} = \begin{array}{r} 22\frac{2}{8} \\ +\ 1\frac{1}{8} \\ \hline 22\frac{3}{8} \end{array}$$

Example: b) Find $22\frac{3}{4} + 1\frac{1}{2}$

Solution:

Step 1

$$\begin{array}{r} 22\frac{3}{4} \\ +\ 1\frac{1}{2} \\ \hline \end{array} = \begin{array}{r} 22\frac{3}{4} \\ +\ 1\frac{2}{4} \\ \hline \end{array}$$

Step 2. $\frac{5}{4} = 1\frac{1}{4}$

Step 3. 23

Step 4. $+\ 1\frac{1}{4}$

$24\frac{1}{4}$

Appendix B

ANOTHER WAY TO SUBTRACT MIXED NUMBERS

This is a useful way to subtract mixed numbers when the whole number parts are large.

1. Write the smaller mixed number underneath the larger.
2. If the bottom fraction is smaller than the top fraction, just subtract the fraction from the fraction and the whole number from the whole number.
3. **However**, if the bottom fraction is larger than the top fraction,
   (a) Subtract 1 from the top whole number.
   (b) Write the 1 you borrowed to the left of the top fraction. Then change this to an improper fraction.
   (c) Finally, subtract the fraction from the fraction, and the whole number from the whole number.

Example: $52\frac{5}{8} - 1\frac{3}{4}$

Solution:

$$\begin{array}{r} 52\frac{5}{8} \\ -\ 1\frac{3}{4} \\ \hline \end{array} = \begin{array}{r} 52\frac{5}{8} \\ -\ 1\frac{6}{8} \\ \hline \end{array} = \begin{array}{r} \overset{51}{5\cancel{2}}\frac{15}{8} \\ -\ 1\frac{6}{8} \\ \hline \end{array} = \begin{array}{r} 51\frac{13}{8} \\ -\ 1\frac{6}{8} \\ \hline 50\frac{7}{8} \end{array}$$

In much the say way you can also subtract fractions from whole numbers:

Example: $2 - \frac{1}{6}$

Solution:

$$\begin{array}{r} 2 \\ -\ \frac{1}{6} \\ \hline \end{array} = \begin{array}{r} \overset{1}{\cancel{2}}\frac{6}{6} \\ -\ \frac{1}{6} \\ \hline \end{array} = \begin{array}{r} 1\frac{6}{6} \\ -\ \frac{1}{6} \\ \hline 1\frac{5}{6} \end{array}$$

Name ______________________________

Date ______________________________

Appendix C

A SHORTCUT FOR SOME MULTIPLICATIONS

We have learned that a fraction can sometimes be reduced to lower terms by **dividing both the numerator and denominator by the same number**. This idea can sometimes be used to make it easier for you to multiply fractions. If you see a numerator and a denominator which have a common divisor (a number that divides both of them exactly):

FIRST: Divide both that numerator and denominator by the common divisor.

SECOND: Then multiply as before.

Example:	a) $\frac{2}{3} \times \frac{7}{4}$
FIRST:	2 will divide 2 and also 4:
	$\frac{\overset{1}{\cancel{2}}}{3} \times \frac{7}{\underset{2}{\cancel{4}}} = \frac{1}{3} \times \frac{7}{2}$
SECOND:	$\frac{1}{3} \times \frac{7}{2} = \frac{7}{6} = 1\frac{1}{6}$

Example:	b) $\frac{1500}{3} \times \frac{8}{4}$
FIRST:	3 will divide 3 and also 1500:
	This gives us $\frac{500}{1} \times \frac{8}{4}$.
	4 will divide 4 and 8.
	This gives us $\frac{500}{1} \times \frac{2}{1}$.
SECOND:	$\frac{500}{1} \times \frac{2}{1} = \frac{1000}{1} = 1000$